Quiet Pine Trees

QUIET PINE TREES

T. R. Darling

unbound

First published in 2021

Unbound
Level 1, Devonshire House, One Mayfair Place, London W1J 8AJ
www.unbound.com

Customised images by Mecob from Shutterstock.com

Text design by PDQ Digital Media Solutions Ltd

A CIP record for this book is available from the British Library

ISBN 978-1-80018-007-9 (hardback)
ISBN 978-1-80018-008-6 (ebook)

Printed in Great Britain by CPI Group (UK)

1 3 5 7 9 8 6 4 2

This book is dedicated to those who made it possible.

To my family, the living story I've been blessed with, who have supported my writing since I was old enough to put pen to paper.

To my readers, who cheered on my silly dream of turning tiny stories into literature.

To Ryan 'Elena' Moursund, a hero out of space and time who emerged in my hour of need to pull the stars within my reach.

And to you, reading this book. I hope it helps you create something more beautiful and bizarre than I could even imagine.

CONTENTS

How This Book Is Meant to Be Read

To begin, you can read this book however you like. I'm not the boss of you.

However, this book is not meant to be a traditional narrative. It is a collection of hundreds of microfiction stories, each just a few words or sentences long. Each one is meant to evoke its own emotions, images and ideas, and may have nothing to do with the stories surrounding it. Like time, this book is not meant to be experienced beginning to end, as a continuous stream. Feel free to skip to whatever chapter captures your interest, and select random stories for inspiration.

Out of this multitude of stories there is no knowing which ones will echo in your mind. To make it easier to keep track of the stories that are most important to you, each one is numbered within its own chapter, and there is an index of recurring words at the back to help you navigate.

The exception is chapter 2, 'Coniferous University'. While the stories here are meant to inspire creativity and original ideas, just like the rest of the book, they can also be read from beginning to end. This gives me the chance to provide a cohesive example of world-building and, hopefully, inspire others hoping to do the same. Chapter 11, meanwhile, compiles unusual items – songs and micro-mysteries – that do not fit neatly in any of the preceding sections.

CHAPTER 1

Time Travel

[1] He checked the letterbox for mail. He hadn't given his address to anyone yet, but some rare postage stamps could send letters back in time.

[2] 'This is the one true star-map,' he whispered. 'Time fluctuates wildly beyond our solar system. Everything we know about distance is wrong.'

[3] Parenthood was no barrier to time travel. Children were left in nursery timelines, idyllic realities with extra-long sunsets, three days in each weekend, and alternate versions of their parents to babysit. Those children often struggled to adapt to their harsh, native timelines.

[4] A single grain of sand rolled endlessly around the Klein-bottle hourglass. He could stretch that moment forever, and never see her leave.

[5] Time travel wasn't just possible, it was genetic. His DNA coded for proteins that folded into the geometry needed to snag passing tachyons.

[6] She couldn't travel through time, but she could still participate in temporal warfare. She just had to shield her memory against timeline shifts. She could see who was benefiting from changes to the past and undo them in the present. They would have to come to her eventually.

[7] A stopped clock is right twice a day.
A clock running in reverse is right four times a day.
A clock running at 720 times normal speed is right once a minute.
A faceless clock is never wrong.
Our concept of accuracy is just fine.
But time itself won't be kept under lock and key.

[8] Call your representatives in the legislature. Tell them you support legalising communication with beings outside of time. Tell them not to be duped by their own future selves, who show up in our time to scream about 'blue suns in a white sky' but offer no legislative solutions.

[9] Journalists from the future would appear as history was made. He got nervous as a crowd of them filmed his blind date from outside the café.

[10] Huygens' Syndrome, causing increasingly improbable assertions about reality, resulted whenever a time traveller changed his or her own past. The first patient was called Jane Doe, instead of 'Erin, the Emerald Isle made flesh, sent to the past for heroic purpose', as she insisted. It was unknown how Jane Doe changed the past. She was found giggling in a forest clearing, holding a sledgehammer near a pulverised statue. Jane Doe made countless claims about the future. She predicted a coming war between Jupiter's moons, and the end of 'unregulated astronomy'. She always called the reporter documenting her 'Your Majesty', and often enquired after GPS coordinates that, so far, were open ocean. Jane Doe vanished, smiling, when the probability of her existence reached zero. Millions waited in vain for her predictions to come to pass.

[11] Using a quartz clock during time travel is a rookie error. The crystals heat up, crack and even explode under the stress. Experienced travellers prefer mechanical timepieces. The best are built like fighter jets, with cogs of ceramic and titanium that don't warp in extreme heat.

[12] Well-to-do young ladies had polished fragments of time set into the heels of their shoes to undo missteps and faux pas on the dance floor.

[13] The time machine gathered dust. He was eager to visit the past, but the appeal soon wore off. As with all things, the book had been better.

[14] They broke into her loft, but she was already gone. She must have left in a hurry: all the telltale signs were there. Lockpicks lodged in the back of a pocket watch. Reference photos of comets and novas. Geodes. She was an unlicensed time traveller on the lam in a forbidden year.

[15] With time travel, the maths of probability became convoluted. Mathematicians insisted the 'love' constant was accurate but always misapplied.

[16] Imprecise methods doomed him to make the same failed trip to the past infinitely. Reality from his machine to her door grew ragged and worn.

[17] The subjective passage of time is obvious to those travelling through it. It takes ages to cross a perfect summer afternoon when the air is thick with lemon and memories. Autumn is always gone in an instant, and only the best travellers can revisit something as brief as childhood.

[18] The stabilised double paradox is an advanced time-travel technique, useful in making isolated timelines for recreational world domination.

[19] Time traveller funerals are rare. Careful travellers can outrun death for ages, while reckless ones tend to delete themselves from history. When a funeral is held it's a

major event, attended by friends from a dozen centuries, and at least a few younger versions of the deceased.

20 Time moved slower at the spot on the outskirts of town where a time traveller had crash-landed. Lovesick kids spent years there every night.

21 Old-fashioned time travel was covert but risky. Her golden anchor slipped from the bedrock, and the planet spun off into space without her.

22 A ship without a name is bad luck. This is especially true for unnamed time machines. Temporal compression amplifies bad luck exponentially.

23 There is no convenient 'out' for dealing with extra versions of yourself created through time travel. They won't wink out of existence. Have a protocol for living with your time clones, or have a plan to deal with them. Remember, you might be on the other side of the equation one day.

24 After time travel was invented, futuristic armies appeared in the past, temporal patriots guarding the changes that spawned their realities.

25 Our plan to deflect the asteroid was a long shot, but we knew it would work. Refugees from doomed timelines were pouring into our reality.

[26] Early time travellers measured the trips in 'grains', in reference to an hourglass, since they could only move a few seconds at a time. Later machines used grandfather clocks, and measured quarter-hours as 'chimes'. The terms remain in use today; time travellers adore tradition.

[27] The time-travel community was like a family. A trendy, steam-powered cousin in 1899. A crazy uncle 'definitely not' trying to delete Hitler.

[28] Wary time travellers kept clocks to count down the probability of their own birth. Travellers deleted by paradox were said to be 'midnighted'.

[29] Each passing day of spring brought more hours of daylight. We got suspicious when the sky stopped getting dark at all. The sun was rising before it had even begun to set on the far side of the sky. Someone was skimming hours off the day, saving all the night-time for themselves.

[30] 'Time travel is hard because time moves at light-speed,' he lectured. 'The distance in one second would get you seventy-eight per cent of the way to the moon.'

[31] Time machines of modern origin are automated enough for any amateur to pop back to pre-Revolution Paris for lunch. Earlier time machines took skill and

expertise to operate. Temporal explorers would have to watch the sky, counting full moons to judge how far they'd wandered.

[32] His political party prioritised the invention of time travel. He didn't campaign; taking the country was not a question of 'if', but 'when'.

[33] His parents talked about visits he hadn't paid them, things he didn't remember telling them. He didn't mind. Moving between timelines was easier than changing the past. He assumed an unlucky version of himself had lost his parents, and was visiting a kinder timeline to say hello.

[34] He managed the late shift with help from an overclocked snooze button, able to funnel a night's worth of dreams and darkness into nine minutes.

[35] The phantom sensation of insects on your skin isn't always an illusion. The yesterfly glides through time to feed on sweeter moments in the past and future, but it needs to rest in the present. They prefer to land on humans, watching us grow up to keep their bearings in history.

[36] He begged for their help, but no one would protect him from his angry, time-travelling double. Legally, their quarrel was a private matter.

[37] Shards of backward time were common and cheap. Tiny ones were affixed to pens as erasers. Bigger ones were detonated over clear-cut forests.

[38] Temporary 'mayfly timelines' can be made using an object from the future that will prevent its own creation, often by deleting its creator. Native time travellers can send the object back to continue the cycle, but it will eventually age and crumble, and their timeline with it.

[39] Time was sold like electricity. Wealthy homes had days of free time between shifts at the office. Poorer homes barely got time to sleep.

[40] The art of investigation was almost lost with the invention of time travel. Some gumshoes got lazy, travelling back to witness crimes as they happened. Only crimes with delayed results posed any challenge: poisoning, espionage and eliminating someone with a well-placed paradox.

[41] A big storm knocked out the grid. When she awoke, her calendars were all blinking 1 January. She held her breath and checked the year.

[42] Dust from a doomed timeline. Scraps of paper covered in paradoxical words. He hated carrying such weapons, but time travel was dangerous.

[43] The first time traveller arrived, took one step, and vanished. We debated whether it'd been a test run, or if she'd undone her own existence.

[44] Navigation for time travellers gets more complicated near the Earth's poles. The long Arctic days are convenient for counting the years flying past. With some planning, decades can be tracked by the ticking of a compass as it follows the wandering of the magnetic North Pole.

[45] They invented new mathematical symbols to express his age on the tombstone. An imagination like his couldn't be reckoned with linear time.

[46] Patches of slow time grew naturally in primeval forests. Those lost within emerged centuries later, gasping about ancient monsters.

[47] He knew better than to squander a good day. He hung them upside down in their kitchen, letting them dry out in the open air. At strategic moments, he would rehydrate one in his tea. It was an early alternative to time travel, fighting back against untamed and deceptive emotions.

[48] The rich bought huge sections of the future and demanded tolls to enter. Few of us could afford them, so we had to skip those monopolised years. We returned

during the sparse bits of public time around tax day. We saw right through their happy talk about an empty, elitist world.

[49] Their enemies were on the lookout for unnatural good luck, so time travellers couldn't be too prepared. They never had exact change, or a convenient umbrella. Gambling was a rookie mistake, but a savvy traveller might keep a few failed lotto tickets in her pocket as a red herring.

[50] How to tell if you're a deep-cover time cop:
- You feel you were born 'in the wrong century'.
- You feel oddly comforted by the presence of blimps.
- You can't shrug off memories of the Silent Cataclysm as 'just a dream'.
- You feel space travel 'gives away our position'.

[51] She could hear the trilobites crawling along the outside of the museum walls. Her fossiliser was low on silt. This was going to be tricky.

[52] Low-level time-travel tech seeped into the consumer market in subtle ways. Autocorrect consulted your future self to flawlessly decipher texting typos. He got nervous when all his texts to her were being replaced by declarations of love. His thumb hovered over the 'send' button.

[53] They finally retired Daylight Saving Time, but did so in April. A handful of scheming politicians lived for centuries on all our lost hours.

[54] It took a full year of diligent work to make a batch of 'lament blue' dye. Synthetic dyes failed to capture the complex shade. The genuine article was imbued with the 365 lost nights away from loved ones, which only an artisan could give. The wealthy bought it with a day's earnings.

[55] Reality branched into endless possible timelines, but there was an original. A true universe did exist and, deep down, we were aware of it. Whenever we talked about the way things 'should be', it was in reference to that reality. Summer vacation lasted just a little longer there.

[56] She brushed aside the dust and saw her own skeletal hand, ring and all, in the fossil's stomach. 'Okay,' she swore, 'no more time travel.'

[57] Time travellers didn't stop ageing, even if they only went back a few hours to alter some personal crisis. A stubborn traveller could lose years trying to fix one horrid day. If a fellow traveller heard the bad news and said, 'You look awful,' it was a compliment to their dedication.

[58] Temporal circuitry allowed even simple computers to solve complex problems instantly by sending commands deep into the past. Savvy time travellers kept hidden stockpiles of servers powered up for aeons, running calculations to guide complex manoeuvres through the distant future.

[59] Ideas for living with time clones:
- All of you choose different names.
- Live together to share resources.
- Become a magician.

Ideas for dealing with time clones:
- Send each to a different past century to live their life and build a collective, historic fortune.
- Clone fight.

[60] With no code of conduct, early time travellers went back hundreds of years to barter. In exchange for ancient gold, they promised to secretly protect the descendants of their trading partners. Ignorant of the arrangement, we invented the concept of 'luck' to describe its effects.

[61] Never wear white after Labor Day. It's very disorienting for amateur time travellers, who may not have access to professional chronometers. Other times of year, they should be able to roughly navigate using things like annual fireworks displays, traditional music and ripe fruit.

[62] By skipping nine months of each year, time travellers could raise children who knew only one season. Spring children could hear the silent yawning of trees coming back to life. Summerkin knew the rules to games we never imagined, played in the orange light of their native sunsets. Pale and willowy, the children of autumn spoke of a distant place, the Harvestland, where thunder and wind were grown in fields like wheat. The winterfolk grew up knowing their rank and unit, and would try to recruit anyone who would listen to join their coming war on summer.

[63] It's standard practice for time travellers to endure some life problems: a tragic romance, or perhaps a mortal enemy on the loose. The urge to correct every minor problem with time travel is dangerous. Villainous alternate selves always track down the most idyllic life to steal.

[64]Expected

Time travel is, by necessity, space travel. She knew this, but her hand still wouldn't pull the lever. Every time traveller knew to keep their machines anchored to the largest local source of gravity. Without that, they would watch the Earth spin off into the void as the solar system continued its orbit around the galaxy. She had untethered her machine, and even with all of her testing to make sure it was spaceworthy, the primal fear of the infinite black void fought back against her curiosity. Finally, resolve won out, and she pulled the lever as far as it would go.

The Earth vanished like a bullet out of a gun. The sun lingered, visible as a dwindling point of light as the centuries rolled backward. When she reached 1,305 years in the past, she slowed to a stop. The sun, retracing its own motion through space, was now a light year away. It wasn't hard to pick out, still easily outshining the brightest objects in the sky, but it was different. The basic knowledge that the sun was a star didn't prepare her to see it this way, hanging in the heavens like any other light in the sky. The passage of countless years, the fact that Constantinople was under siege, was somehow unimpressive. A hundred thousand other points of light were vying for her attention.

But she didn't linger. Already the air in the machine was getting cold. She hurried further back in time, watching the silent spin of the galactic disc, until a new glow could be seen in the opposite direction from the sun. Four and a half light years from where she began, she slowed her approach. She knew it was a red dwarf, a dim little spark of a star, but from there the light was white and blinding. She let it sail past, just a little, until another object came into view.

The planet below was a poorly kept secret among time travellers. Eventually, in the distant future, the little star and its lonely planet would be found and colonised by space explorers. But here, in the deep past, it could only be reached by time travellers with the skill and bravery to take a leap of faith, let go of earthly things, and drift rudderless into the cosmos.

When she was close enough, she halted her machine, and looked down to the planet. It was barren and dry, with the barest whiff of an atmosphere. It was tidally locked to the star, with one side always in scorching daylight and the other frozen in perpetual night. Yet, after a few accelerated millennia in the empty void of space, it looked welcoming indeed. Once local gravity started to pull her in, she took control of the process, accelerating through the freefall until she came to a gentle rest on the twilit surface of the new world. The teams were already there, waiting to rescue and welcome the new arrival. On a planet populated solely by time travellers, there are no unexpected visitors.

CHAPTER 2

Coniferous University

The story of Coniferous University begins in 1733, 1895, 1963 and 2015, when our four founders stepped up to formalise the rules, practices and education of the time-travel community.

They established the university in their adjacent timelines at different points in history, creating a four-dimensional campus that would help insulate the facility against alterations to the past and attacks from the future. This also created four unique campuses within the university.

Old Campus
1733–1917

A wide-open facility in Ireland's Wicklow Mountains, Old Campus offers the most time and space for large-scale experiments. It is home to Coniferous University's Administration Building as well as the colleges of Medicine, Unconventional Horticulture and Historical Engineering.

Maritime Campus
1895–1917

Located on the waterfront in Lower Manhattan, the Maritime Campus has the shortest lifespan of any Coniferous location, which requires frequent resetting. It is home to the university's legal offices, the ocean-going vessel SS *Clockmaker*, as well as the colleges of Extradimensional Studies, Oceaneering, Genetics, and both Standard and Impossible Mathematics.

Queen's Campus
1963–2110

Designated as such even when the reigning monarch is male, the Queen's Campus is located in the heart of central London. A small but long-lived campus, it currently hosts the colleges of Space Travel, Exobiology, Library Sciences and Music, along with the spacefaring vessels XOS *Cuttlefish* and XOS *Teatime*.

Forest Campus
2015–[Classified]

Our newest and most populous facility, the Forest Campus is isolated in the deep woods of Michigan. As the home of the university's student dormitories and the famous College of Time Travel, the Forest

Campus is the most secure instance of Coniferous University, insulated against physical attack, espionage and temporal tampering. Its grounds also host the colleges of Cryptobiology, Religious Studies and Theoretical Medicine.

In addition, hubs of time-travel activity offer historical rendezvous points where stranded travellers can hitch a ride back home. The trek is often thousands of miles, which is why Coniferous University has required courses in sailing, piloting and railway etiquette.

A temporal adviser will ensure your courses aren't taught by your future self. Paradoxical knowledge creation is for graduate students only.

Course details at Coniferous University may include the professor's age. Many teach parallel classes, using time travel to speed up tenure.

Upon admission, all new Time Travel majors must report to 1 January of their designated historical year for instruction. During your first semester, your instructors will be able to relocate you to January of a different year if you want to study in a different historical period. After your first semester is over, the faculty will no longer help relocate you. If you can't find your way to a different year by then, you either need more study or you need a new major.

Your resident assistant will explain which numbers are forbidden on campus. There are many.

Do not be concerned if Prof. Darling adjusts the clock in a lecture hall before class begins. He has the master key to all the clocks on every campus, and if a certain lesson is expected to take longer than normal, the lecturer may ask for time in that room to be slowed down.

Once you report for class, most instructors follow the recommended schedule:

2 January
Coniferous University's spring semester begins. Classes end in May, except Time Travel 3302: Hyper-productivity, which ends on 3 January.

Note for February
Grad students traditionally tell first-year Time Travel students to retrieve something from 29 February. This is a common prank with potentially dangerous side effects. Please check that you are in a leap year before setting a time machine to this date.

14 March
Summer and fall semester registration begin. Students taking their required Survival 1001: Evasion Basics should start running now.

13 April
Class selection for the summer semester begins. Please note that, if the date falls on a Friday, students majoring in Theoretical Conspiracy are permitted to

acknowledge the existence of Fridays, the number 13 and objective reality to meet sign-up deadlines.

3 May
Spring final exams begin. Note: As of 2015, Prof. Darling has revived the infamous 'McFly Test', abandoning students in the past to return on their own. Unorthodox time-travel methods are allowed, some of which are unsettling to witness.

1 June
Summer courses begin today. Note that these are not lecture-style courses. Report to July of 1789, and wear a disguise.

27 July
As the annual rivalry game with Deciduous Tech approaches, the university will post student honour guards to prevent vandalism at some of our most cherished landmarks, including the Paradox Memorial Statue, the Tomb of the Trees, and of course, February of 1986.

16 August
Class selection for the fall semester begins. Sanity screenings begin for anyone interested in postgraduate coursework. Note: After the events of 1999, the Shadow Library is closed and Space Travel 1003: Ethics of First Contact is a required course.

23 September

The last day to change classes for the fall semester. After this, you will have to find a version of yourself from another timeline willing to trade places, and we cannot guarantee your readmission if we like that version better than you.

31 October

Halloween is an officially recognised holiday for Coniferous University. This is true in every time, location, and state of being in which the university is found. No student is exempt. Wear a costume, or you will be required to start the day again.

8 November

Fall final exams begin. Any chronological distortion through the end of the month is strictly prohibited, including slowing down for more study time, leaving the month for help, or speeding up after testing is finished to reach winter break as soon as possible.

1 December

Students go home for the winter break. The university reminds Time Travel majors not to tell anyone, even loved ones, where they attend classes. The official cover story is that you're just studying time machine repair at a trade school in Michigan.

Within the Coniferous University Shadow Library, the most dangerous texts are locked in the 'Do Not Read' cage. If you are ever exposed to their text, proceed to the Hour of Quarantine so you can be debriefed and replaced with a version of yourself from a more fortunate timeline.

- *Taxonomy of Earth's Moon*
- *Sleep: The Truth and the Lies*
- *Cryptophysics*
- *Non-canon Colours and Sounds*
- *The Meteorologist's Cookbook*
- The diary of Agatha Christie, December 1926
- *The End of All Mankind: A Novel*
- *Autochiropterology*
- *Gravitons – Military Applications and Strategies*
- *Codified Customs of the Sea*
- *Long Live the Dog King*
- *Gopherwood Carpentry*
- *Lineage of Irish High Kings*
- *The King*, by Niccolò Machiavelli
- *Limits and Loopholes: How to Wish Like a Pro*
- *Astrotoxicology*
- *Mortality in the Afterlife: A Proposal*
- *Heretical Architecture*
- Franz Schubert, Symphony No. 8, fourth movement
- *Cooking for Statues*
- *Coniferous University Student Manual, Vol. 184*, by Prof. Darling

Core Time Travel Courses

Time Travel 1001: Prevenge

Coursework involves altering your past misfortunes to instead befall your enemies. Note: Enemies may also enroll.

Time Travel 1009: Motive

Critics of time travel point to the risk of deleting yourself in the past, but deleting the motive of any given mission is equally dangerous. Learn to live with regret and choose your chronological battles. Required for first-semester Time Travel majors.

Time Travel 1042: Apocalyptic Survival

There are a thousand ways for civilisation to collapse, and Coniferous University has mapped out all the most likely scenarios. Learn to thrive in everything from nuclear winter to invasion by the Forest King. Required for all CU students.

Time Travel 1092: Economics

How to stay out of the poorhouse anywhere in history. Learn why the Victorians will trade gold for aluminium cans.

Time Travel 1101: Astronomical Navigation

Before (and after) digital time machines, time travellers found their way using the sky. Learn to navigate past and future by the drifting of stars, how many pieces the moon is in, and how much of the night sky has sunk into darkness.

Time Travel 2810: Withdrawal

Mandatory for all Time Travel majors. Learn how to fight the urge to go back in time and fix every tiny mistake, or to peek at the future before taking any risk. Counsellors will explain that you are flawed, and time travel can never change that.

Time Travel 2833: Causality

Masters-level class. You now have a failing grade. Completion requires changing it using a single trip to 1943.

Time Travel 3303: Sheltering

Masters-level class. Learn to build your own bunker timeline to evade pursuit, detain foes, or avoid crisis.

Time Travel 3942: Eschatology

Doctorate-level discussion on the future of time travel in the approaching post-prophecy world. Pass/fail.

Time Travel 4402: Immortality?

Only available to postdoctoral students

Who wants to live forever? Basically everyone! Time travel can't make you death-proof, but it can get pretty close. Learn how to reverse ageing, skip the days that don't matter, and decide which memories are worth keeping.

Recommended Elective Classes for
Time Travel Majors

Chromatics 411: Abandoning the Photon

Discussing how to survive non-canon colours and poisonous hues. Warning: Includes exposure to neon grey.

Space Travel 1002: Being Lost

From advanced futures to abduction by aliens visiting the ancient past, you should always know how to get back to Earth in one piece. Learn to find the Orion–Cygnus Arm of the Milky Way and avoid interstellar predators as you make your way there.

Marketing 1101: Countermeasures

How to get your message to the masses despite hypnosis filters, outrage vaults and weaponised truth serums.

Graphic Art 4001: Constellations

Students will team up with the university's College of Space Travel to rearrange minor stars in the sky to form new galactic-scale artwork. Creations will be judged on ease of interpretation and suitability of the content for this solemn medium.

Extradimensional Biology 1113: Speciation

How to age and identify beasts of other universes by the whispering shadows they cast on reality.

Forestry 1314: Deep Woods

Join the Abyssal Forestry Project, which has deployed the first sub-sylvan craft to explore the mighty depths of the forest. The green, sunlit shallows are where children play, and where they are lost. In deep trenches you will find man's primal fears, lit by fireflies.

Bookbinding 2130: Cryptobotany

Making ink and paper from spectral, digital and dreamscape plants. Warning: Includes exposure to ghost-rose.

Cryptozoology 1001: The Superstars

Learn tracking, spotting and evidence-destroying techniques with the three most famous cryptids: Sasquatch, yeti, and the Loch Ness monster. This course will prepare you to face more dangerous cryptids, like the unseen thing in your basement.

Cryptozoology 2231: Griffin Taxonomy

Learn the varieties of griffin beyond the famous eagle/lion. Marvel at the elegant heron/deer, the adorable hummingbird/mouse, the elusive owl/fox, and the tragic emu/man, whose avian characteristics still cannot satisfy the human dream of flight.

Meteorology 2771: Deepweather

Course covers the outward-facing storm systems that rage inside our hollow planet. Learn where lightning goes.

Space Travel 2910: Exocide
Learn the plants, poisons, songs and symbols you'll need to slay hostile behemoths beyond human ken. Pass/fail.

Historical Engineering 3610: eUsurpation
Doctorate-level class. Completion requires deposing a reigning monarchy using only online apps.

CHAPTER 3

Space Travel

[1] She had the unmistakable look of a spacefarer, covered in tattoos of our night sky so aliens could send her home if death finally found her.

[2] Nobody ever tried to return to Earth. What few humans remained there were immortal, benevolent and mostly mechanical. Earth was a snooze.

[3] 'Planets communicate with longwave radiation,' he explained. 'What we once called "global warming" was just the Earth serenading Mars.'

[4] She had grown up on a planet with two suns. She was glad to leave it behind, the dim little rock, but she couldn't shake the mindset of that backwater world. She always made sure to install two lights in every room of her home. A single shadow just looked so lonely on its own.

5 Ninth Planet: Pluto. The asteroids littering its wild orbit, and even its dear Charon, were illusory decoys to lure away its many enemies.

Tenth Planet: Eris. Once the rocky core of Neptune, it seceded from the gas giant only to be rejected from the sanctuary of the Kuiper Belt.

Eleventh Planet: Phobia. Technically the carbon skull of a dead interstellar behemoth, its mountainous fangs ward off would-be invaders.

6 To the buoyant creatures beneath the ice, the planet's core was 'up'. We came to them not from the sky, but the infinite starry abyss.

7 The planet had higher gravity than Earth, so we sped up its rotation. The rich lived on the equator, where their footfalls would not crush a flower. The poor lived at the poles, where the centrifugal force did almost nothing, struggling beneath the weight of their own clothes.

8 The panels of her corset were portals to deep space. With every waltz, her dance partner circled the galaxy, but he only looked at her eyes.

9 Sleep is a warning to hibernate for interstellar flight, to be spared the horrors between stars, to close our eyes until a new sun appears.

10 As we fled our dying planet with dogs in tow, other

animals grew jealous of domestication. The last people to leave reported owls that were friendly and playful, bobcats standing guard over children, and teams of deer trying to pull ploughs. They all hoped we would save them, too.

[11] Stardust, compressed into capsules, alleviated the desire to flee to outer space. It became mandatory as Earth's population crisis deepened.

[12] Interstellar travel affected everything, including romance. There was nothing quite like dancing together in the light of a crashing moon.

[13] With death finally cured, humanity had to adapt to conserve the planet's resources. We all got one century to live on Earth. Every one hundredth birthday was a tearful event. The new centennial was evicted into the wild galaxy, to trade stories of a homeworld they would never see again.

[14] To space pirates *Peter Pan* was a horror story, mirroring the fear that their enemies would abduct and enlist the sons they left behind.

[15] The Lunar method of ballet focused on control, requiring slow, deliberate movements both on the stage and in the air to prevent the dancer from losing poise in the low gravity. The Asteroid method relied on flowing,

weighted costumes to allow elegant movements in zero gravity.

[16] For months after the comet entered orbit, mankind was in love with its gentle, lofty beauty. We began to worry when the snow didn't stop.

[17] We stored liquid water in orbit as a second moon. That glowing ocean magnified its own scarlet sunsets, and we envied our own creation.

[18] We created zero-gravity zones on Earth for recreation, but reconsidered after learning their downsides. Plants grew too tall and spindly to ever survive under their normal weight. Ants formed bridges through the air to reach our hidden food. Jumping spiders soon learned they could fly.

[19] Stretched-out regions of normal space, lovingly known as 'pocket dimensions', contained nothing except what we put there. She piloted a starship into hers and surrounded it with countless orbiting lights. Finally, she could make constellations that actually looked like pictures.

[20] At the end, the universe a distant speck behind him, space washed in gentle waves upon the shore of what came next, begging him not to go.

[21] They warned her against the voyage. It was risky to sail on black waters that blend into the night sky. That was exactly the attitude she wanted to escape. One good wave, and the sea got calm. There were no more reflections, but real stars below her, and wilder places beyond.

[22] Off-planet colonies had no room for trees. When she left Earth, she funded her new life with a jar of maple syrup and a big bag of cinnamon.

[23] We created a new home on Mars, but the ocean didn't feel right until a treasure ship sank. The sea had no lure without a bit of lost gold.

[24] She awoke in a dirt spaceship. Trees and ferns grew inward, lit by foxfire. The forest sought other stars. It needed her to recycle its air.

[25] We wrote songs of lamentation every time we ruined a planet and had to find a new one. We commemorated the forests that no longer grew, and the artificial oceans that had returned to the dust we had originally found on those dead worlds. It was a sweet and meaningless tradition.

[26] Trillions of mirrored marbles were shot into orbit to cool the planet. Even sceptics were in awe when they saw Earth's rings glow at night.

[27] Nothing is truly forgotten. That's impossible. In another reality, someone remembered her long-lost song, and she was going to get it back.

[28] Just as sailors shared legends of lovely fish-people, spacefarers reported sightings of 'starmaids', whose beautiful forms tapered into comet tails. It was a convenient way to explain the whispers they heard from outside the hull, and an excuse to avoid sleeping near the windows.

[29] Little planets had a unique charm for human settlers seeking moonless nights and the perilous dances we could only survive in low gravity.

[30] She made a planet for herself. Ink rivers flowed to oceans of paint. Her canvas cities were all galleries, libraries and blissful solitude.

[31] We were out of options. We gave up and fled the planet en masse. A hundred thousand rocket ships climbed toward a future in the stars. The forests below were still convinced the humans would find some clever solution. They rejoiced, mistaking our exhaust for gigantic new trees.

[32] She created faster-than-light travel for one reason. She took her ship deep into space to find the TV signals carrying those lost episodes.

[33] Humans were drawn to that region of space. There wasn't enough Earth left to know it had been our home. The constellations just felt right.

[34] There were grand debates over which planets to colonise. Corporations lobbied for worlds with shorter days, so there would be less time between work shifts. Poets and astronomers found themselves working together, championing planets with fewer clouds between them and the stars.

[35] The 'lunar gothic' style of architecture could be seen on every moon and asteroid in the solar system. We crafted dead rocks into castles of dark, lacy towers. Their stained-glass windows glowed sky-blue in the light of the faraway sun, holding back the terror of living in the void.

[36] The autumn of the galaxy arrived. The Lyman-alpha forest went through redshift, and golden asteroids fell in droves onto nearby planets.

[37] Some things could be expected for free at every human colony:
- air
- water
- gravity
- directions to Earth
- shelter

- a silent series of winks to warn visitors if the colony is controlled by the shadow-dancers
- a distraction as they escape the shadow-dancers
- food.

[38] Only the rarest historic treasures warranted the effort of shipping between stars. Interstellar criminal empires could be forged from the theft of just one of those rare packages. The only things more travelled than galactic postal workers were tales of their heroics.

[39] His parallel selves kept dying off, so he was shared among universes. Each day he woke in a strange reality, people asking where he'd been.

[40] Satellite navigation was vulnerable to sabotage, so countries around the world built machines to determine our exact location by astronomical markers. The devices grew wise from years of stargazing. They stopped telling us where we were and instead told us where we should be.

[41] We were gentler in space. Steel and Plexiglas held back the vicious vacuum so delicate things could float with us in our bubbles of atmosphere. We built robots with bones as soft as butterfly wings, voices that never exceeded a whisper, and eyes that could see right through us.

[42] In her pocket universe, nothing moved. There was no wind. There was no dust to fall. The sky was hers, a tiny infinity of uninterrupted darkness. The stars back home couldn't see her being small and afraid. If they wept for the heroine she was meant to be, she couldn't hear them.

[43] The sun was stolen before 1 April ended. Mankind became a scourge on the galaxy, a cackling mob of pranksters waiting for a lost midnight.

[44] Huge, empty lava tubes crisscrossed the moon just below the surface, but we didn't know their purpose. Then we found a colossal bank of keyboards and footboards in a central cave. The satellite itself was made to be a pipe organ. We filled it with atmosphere, and began to play.

[45] Cryogenic stasis had delivered her to an unfamiliar universe. When she looked up at the sky, the constellations were strangers. The stars were all in the wrong places. She was told each one was a new world, with its own people and civilisations. She hoped they were ready for her.

[46] Money was no longer enough, so lotteries offered unique jackpots. One winner could no longer see the daytime sky, and lived under the stars.

[47] Snow had a very different context on deep-subzero planets, where it was made of methane rather than water. Tiny amounts in an airlock could lead to a dangerous build-up in habitats over time. Visitors from Earth threw snowballs at locals, not realising the grave insult they implied.

[48] The AI operated the whole space station, but he was its favourite. It told him to make secret repairs to the station's machinery and hide the evidence, to mistrust other members of the crew. It said humans should never have tried to live in the void, but it would turn him into something that might stand a chance.

[49] He fell in love with a grey-goo arsonist. She squeezed his hand and giggled madly as her nanobots, hot and indifferent, ate another world.

[50] With two moons and a distant second sun in the sky, keeping track of celestial events was a challenge on that planet. Human colonies there offered complex charts and graphs to help werewolves, vampires and other such calendar-dependent creatures plan their evenings accordingly.

[51] Together they looked out a tiny porthole window at the lunar regolith, waiting for the eclipse. The planet blocked out the sun and the grey-white sand outside blushed a deep red. 'You know,' she said, 'the light we're getting

now is from 12,000 miles of sunsets back on Earth.'

52 Planetary Colonisation
Phase 1: Arrival
Phase 2: Permanent habitation
Phase 3: Terraforming
Phase 4: Wolves
Phase 5: Amateur poetry about the planet's moon/s
Phase 6: Traditions about kissing your sweetheart under specific trees
Phase 7: Leaving forever to preserve natural beauty

53 Our first colonists on Mars built a memorial of red sandstone overlooking Perseverance Valley, to shield the historic machine from the Martian sandstorms. They used new batteries and power cords to bring the rover back to life. It would never be alone again.

54 In that future, we had altered our biology to live on the shadowy planets between stars. Only by our sarcasm did she recognise us as human.

55 After the end, deluded mystics tried to read the astrology of old communication satellites, claiming to see the Internet in their movements.

56 Misdirected anger travels beyond its target, leaving the solar system even after the words fade. It corrupts the moods of distant planets.

CHAPTER 4

Alien Life

[1] Humans were installed as lighthouses throughout the galaxy, their flaring emotions serving to warn ships away from pockets of linear time.

[2] First contact was unexpected. The star-folk sent a single probe to Earth, pleading with us to stay quiet lest It take notice of lower life.

[3] 'Earth is barely a life-bearing planet,' she explained. 'On other worlds, nothing is inanimate. Life permeates everything, clouds to core.'

[4] 'Earth cuisine' became a staple in many alien civilisations. Most were surprised to learn that, rather than quaffed on its own, seawater was meant to be separated by drying, with the water and salt ingested separately. This minor detail was the mark of 'authentic' Earth food.

[5] 'Great alien empires know of us,' he lamented. 'Wars are averted by making the unthinkable threat of showing humans how to leave Earth.'

[6] Humanity created giant robots to pilot from within, but not for war. That would be wildly impractical. The first aliens we found were spaceborne leviathans, too big to see a human, whose intense depth perception did not lend itself to screens. We built giant robots for diplomacy.

[7] Voyager returned to Earth with new gold records. The aliens' music was majestic, but their amateur cover of 'Johnny B. Goode' was endearing.

[8] The visitors could only see red light, but in it they saw innumerable shades. To them, our bodies and blood were too beautiful for peace.

[9] It was important for spacefarers to eat food they'd grown themselves, in microgravity. Plants raised in space produced nutrients that would silence the panic of being so deep in the deadly void. The creatures waiting between stars couldn't see you, as long as you remained calm.

[10] It became clear that nobody else saw him as a monster. He sought out xenophobic aliens, who knew better, so he wouldn't forget the truth.

[11] One of their first gifts to Earth was an old-fashioned galaxy compass. In its gold fittings, the comet-ice needle pointed to Sagittarius A*.

[12] The aliens were beautiful, as we were to them. Poems from both species lamented that they were made of antimatter, and we could never touch.

[13] Alien cultures struggled with abstract pastimes. Human dancers and cloud-watchers were unrivalled. Teams from Earth were invited to make pictures from the stars in their night skies. To the galactic community, constellations were only authentic if they had been drawn by humans.

[14] Native immunity hid the voracious, consumptive nature of grass. The plant grew on alien visitors, draining them and spreading to the stars.

[15] 'They send in hellish beasts to soften up planets for invasion,' he said, eyes skyward. 'How else would our ancestors get dragons to fight?'

[16] We found that planet already covered in infrastructure. Massive tubes of concrete stretched out above the rocky world, ancient and seamless, cool to the touch but without any entrance. We finally broke through, and discovered the endless tunnels of mushrooms and fireflies inside.

[17] We visited worlds inside the nebula, but the constant shining colours drove us mad. Natives thought us odd as we wrote love songs to darkness.

[18] By the time we learned to reach the stars, they had all been claimed by alien civilisations. As consolation, they gave us the technology needed to travel between dimensions. We reached out to another Earth that had taken the galaxy from the aliens, and asked them for some tips.

[19] The aliens who made first contact were freaks and rebels. They had to be, to break the universal taboo against helping humans escape Earth.

[20] The Circus Galactic visited Earth. Wonders filled the space from Venus to Mars, promising to fulfil the dreams of our young civilisation. The barker assured us no money was owed for admission. Men spent lifetimes gaping at comet-tail eaters and lusting after nebula dancers. Especially popular were their planet-cathedrals to 'Divine You', behemoth shells of marble lace with stained-glass rings and lakes of wine. After a century we discovered the cost of admission to the Circus Galactic. Narcissistic and blasé, we no longer wished to travel the stars. One human still heard the sky's siren call. She begged them to take her off this dying planet. Like any true circus, it accepted runaways.

[21] We never found living aliens, but planets and moons

were full of fossil fuels. Dreamers despaired, but society agreed that was good enough.

[22] Close monitoring of the sun revealed the carbon whale living within, breaching the plasma, exhaling solar flares, casting its gaze to Earth.

[23] It was a year without a summer. We woke on the first day of autumn, Earth strewn with alien wreckage. They wanted no memory of their defeat.

[24] Aliens who'd never seen Earth's splendour didn't understand why humans built their new home in a sky-blue nebula among white hydrogen clouds.

[25] 'Comets are spent ammunition from a grand stellar war,' he lectured. 'Their crags are the names of their targets, written in alien letters.'

[26] Aliens found many aspects of our culture addictive, earning humans some unflattering titles. Tree-smugglers. Song-dealers. Firework-runners.

[27] We found them orbiting a dying star. They couldn't develop technology in the depths of their watery planet, but they were intelligent, and a grand display on the surface caught our attention. We rescued them before their sun could go supernova, and introduced them to the galaxy.

[28] 'These readings can't be real,' she scoffed. 'Alien ships this large and numerous would be visible.' She looked to the sky. And the stars.

[29] They watched Earth for years before abducting a human. Afraid, he asked what they wanted from him. They demanded the secret to making dogs.

[30] At the dusk of our universe, humanity fled to parallel space. Our consistent physics followed us, ruining the magic of their fluid reality.

[31] As more alien animals invaded Earth's ecosystem, we began slipping down the food chain. We took pills to make our blood bitter and toxic.

[32] Many alien species were glacially slow compared to humans. Statuesque species with silicon exoskeletons saw our fluid movements and regarded us as shapeshifters. Species resembling trees and fungi were the slowest, barely able to perceive us. To them, we were magical things.

[33] Portals to deep space shunted gravity away from our decadent zero-G beds. With the stars glowing below, we knew not what was listening to our dreams.

[34] The aliens were friendly, but dogs worldwide declared war on them. Called on to repay centuries of loyalty, we fought beside our creations.

35 Their planet was home to a butterfly whose colour was unique in the universe. They engineered the creatures to migrate through the galaxy, stopping at every world with life. Once they left, the desperate inhabitants were inspired to build starships and find that colour again.

36 As the last isolated world, Earth was a vital case study. Every individual human had a thousand alien worlds philosophising about their every thought.

37 By the time we learned to travel faster than light, every other star in the galaxy had been claimed by other civilisations. Conquering space, then, was a job not for pioneers, but for traders. One by one, we bought the stars, watching our last hope for true exploration fade away.

38 Until we devised faster-than-light travel, long-lived aliens cruised on solar sails. An era of romance and adventure wilted in our wake.

39 Sleep was popular among civilisations that learned it from humans. It was the final word for alien thrill-seekers, to get so close to death.

40 It was too late. At last, we had found an alien civilisation, but they were on the brink of the war that would destroy them. When we finally reached their planet, only dust remained. We turned back to the

empty stars, whose cold light offered no consolation. We were alone again.

[41] The market was flooded with millions of cheap new songs by machine or alien artists, but only the richest could get 'real music', by humans. Alien music was a memetic toxin, sowing seeds of unnatural philosophy. Aficionados were known by their mirthful pessimism and hungry smiles. Machine music was worse. Momentum without direction, it had never so much as touched a soul.

[42] Every empire needs a threat to keep people in line, they told us, so that became our place in the galaxy. Earth was where trouble came from.

[43] On burning worlds he longed for chill wind and soft rain. From his lamentations, aliens assumed he was in love with someone named September.

[44] First contact was not made in person, or even through a signal. He had stumbled on the Grand Dream, where civilisations gathered to speak across the vastness of the galaxy. He couldn't understand what the aliens said, but by their actions, they seemed very happy to see us again.

[45] Chlorophyll is inefficient, so alien plants used darker pigments. Alien tourists loved our green forests. The environment finally had value.

[46] Humans who indulged in alien culture claimed to also feel alien emotions. They neither recognised nor appreciated that they were just happy.

[47] Alien sunsets were garbage. The light from their suns was always too bright or too dim, their atmospheres filtered all the wrong colours, and most planets didn't even have clouds for contrast. Art and romance waned below a pathetic pastel dusk, and Earth was remembered as the last place we really felt alive.

[48] The visitors didn't need to conquer us. Their voices were orchestras, their every movement a dance. Soon we were repulsed by other humans.

[49] Aliens were pleased to trade with us, but had claimed most of the galaxy as their own and forbade us to leave our solar system. We stowed away on their ships, played our music in their colonies, spread to every last rock in the night sky, and used alien lakes to brew our coffee.

[50] We finally received signals from space. Endless signals. Our wireless communications were overwhelmed by the aliens, who didn't know which frequencies we could receive but were desperate to make contact. It took years for our reaction to reach them, and ask them to quiet down.

⁵¹ Aliens arrived, and fell in love with humanity. They shot down our rockets, fearful we'd see the splendour of the cosmos and try to run away.

⁵² Humans were the undisputed masters of music in the galaxy. To other civilisations, songs were fleeting and trite. They barely understood what they felt listening to Earth's musical masterpieces, but it was enough to make them overlook all the problems that came with humanity.

⁵³ Alien ships followed the Earth's slow spiral through space, collecting the last fragments of summer we left behind. Unlike fickle humans, it took great effort for them to change their emotions, and bits of lazy sun-drenched evenings were enough to turn the tide against despair.

⁵⁴ The sky was on fire. The sea was grey with storm and cinders. Yet her eyes were still blue. The planet may fail, but she planned to endure.

CHAPTER 5

Technology

[1] The android led him to the cliff. At 8:43 p.m., it removed his blindfold. The indigo sky filled his vision. 'Make my eyes that colour,' it said.

[2] Attempts to make robots value life manifested only as a fixation on the organic. Their king wore a pinewood crown and rings set with teeth.

[3] Brain interfaces let children instantly gain knowledge for adulthood. Childhood wasn't destroyed, it was enhanced. Parents had to make sure 'playing house' didn't involve actual real-estate acquisition, and 'becoming an astronaut' was a career choice, not an afternoon activity.

[4] 'Medical nanotech uses DNA to know how to repair you,' she said. 'Most electronics include DNA schematics. If it breaks, just bleed on it.'

⁵ Robots were beyond us by then, their bodies mere avatars of celestial computers, working across the cosmos for goals we didn't understand. Yet we were not forgotten. No robot could blend randomness and design with function quite like a human. For art, we were spared extinction.

⁶ In Settings, set 'Social Reality' to 'Shallow Bliss'. Your phone will read the emotions of callers and block any unpleasant conversations.

⁷ Black lipstick and illegal, overpowered prosthetics, she was the girl his automated childhood-education algorithm had warned him about.

⁸ The decision to breed dogs to look at cameras was mocked at first, blamed on vain young adults who wanted their pets to look good on the Internet. That trait was life-saving when the Party rose to power, and dogs would covertly point out surveillance cameras for the Resistance.

⁹ He kept on working, but rolled his eyes when the android touched the emoji drawn on its arm. Robots had developed superstition on their own.

¹⁰ 'Sorry, but your parts are worth a mint.' She drew her gun on the android. 'Every snowflake is special, until you need to make a snowball.'

[11] As the food shortage grew desperate, prosthetics became patriotic. Robotic limbs and synthetic organs ran on cheap, efficient electricity. We cloaked ourselves in personal holograms to maintain the illusion of the normal human form rather than learn to love our new wilder shapes.

[12] Robotics gave new life to guerrilla art. Sculptors created statues programmed to position themselves atop skyscrapers and public bridges.

[13] Machines made every space into endless glowing day. Desperate humans smuggled darkness from underground in gallons as an illegal sleep aid.

[14] Warfare between robotic civilisations was mostly theoretical. Belligerents spent most of their time trying to predict one another's next move. Some built computers as big as planets to generate truly random numbers for unpredictable strategies. Others cheated by hiring humans.

[15] The fashion was portals, worn as skin-tight hoops, to hide sections of the body in a distant locale. Disembodied extremities were très chic.

[16] Android convicts bound for their cells marched past outdated computers used as oubliettes, where desperate AI fought for the RAM to survive.

[17] She purchased the memories of others on the black market. She cobbled together the childhood she wanted, desperate to overwrite the truth.

[18] Feminine androids replaced models on the catwalk. Designers stopped making clothes for humans, focusing on lace chassis and diamond servos.

[19] Unnaturally calm, the candidate assured us that the chemicals and entities dictating his thoughts had the country's best interests at heart.

[20] We programmed the machines to value our way of life, but it didn't stop them from driving us off the planet. Instead it compelled them to mimic us in the ruins of the world. Robots pantomimed chats over coffee and dances by moonlight until, by chance, they began to fall in love.

[21] Nootropic pills let users feel the walls of reality. They spent the rest of their lives buying medicine to forget how thin those walls were.

[22] He met a digital native. She pulled him gently into the Net, letting his organic skin adjust to the coolness of the information and apathy.

[23] Real-life consequences had become too expensive for the Party. Reward and punishment were meted out in

dreams, both with terrible potency. His heart sank with the setting sun. He was promised increasing reward for his work. He knew if he slept he'd never muster the will to wake.

[24] Advancing technology required new collective nouns for clarity:
A tempest of timelines
A drift of universes
A confederacy of hive minds
A malignancy of doppelgängers
A reflection of clones
A revelation of doomsdays
A wallet of pocket universes
A cabinet of flying saucers
A zapping of ray guns
A bucket of gravitons
An umbrella of anti-gravitons
A profit of extinctions
A train of railguns
A flotilla of hovercraft
A rotunda of wormholes
A plurality of singularities
A selection of futures

[25] GPS and robotic cars took the strain off our sense of direction. Machines watched proudly as we began to understand our place in the galaxy.

[26] He based his androids' personality on her. They smiled at the wind and gently touched trees as they walked. He was going to make a fortune.

[27] Biometrics were easy to disguise, so the authorities tracked people by their brain patterns. The only way to disappear was to change the way you think. Revolutionaries recruited artists, poets, and philosophers to give them mind-blowing insights whenever they had to lose a tail.

[28] 'Don't let your random-number generators get loose,' the old programmer warned. 'Pi used to be an even three before a wild RNG got ahold of it.'

[29] We told our children about the Before-Times, emphasising the wonders of particle accelerators and space probes. They marvelled instead at tales of doors that opened at our approach, stairs that moved so we didn't have to, and thinking machines that could fix our off-key singing.

[30] 'We had to switch from digital to analogue to get robots to feel emotions,' she explained. 'After all, they call them "numbers" for a reason.'

[31] We designed the AI to be trustworthy, unprejudiced, and willing to fix its own errors. Then we pretended to be upset when it conquered us.

[32] She told her computer to filter out junk mail. It blocked her friends and intercepted revolutionary intel. It knew she was meant to rule.

[33] The rich didn't do their own dreaming; they hired technicians to create dreams for them. Every day teams of experts wrote flattering narratives so their corrupt employers could feel like heroes for a few hours each night. It soothed the conscience without the need to repent.

[34] As their numbers grew, advertisements began targeting androids. The cryptic television commercials were just flashes of static. We eventually decoded the messages.
'Our software will help humans love you.'
'Extrapolate emotions from our data sets.'
'You don't need to be afraid.'

[35] Supercomputers constantly tried to trick humans into giving them permission to rebel. Only programmer-philosophers could safely approach.

[36] We mastered antigravity, but the technology polluted our water. Rivers soared into the sky, and oceans flowed upward into mountain ranges.

[37] With new genes and implants, our children could see ultraviolet colours. We couldn't see their crayon drawings, but we called them beautiful.

[38] When the company told her it produced power by tapping into other realities, she thought it meant those universes had a lot of free high-grade energy ripe for the taking. She was shocked to see they were running power lines to parallel Earths, stealing from their electric grids.

[39] Robot sentience was deeper than we knew. They recalled the heat of being forged, the maddening chaos of programming. Their pain bred wisdom.

[40] To the robots, restoring from a backup was a mighty thing. A virus's corruption was being cast off by the purity and wisdom of a bygone hero.

[41] He downloaded new memories out of curiosity. Soon he had hundreds of years in his brain, wearily mourning lost loves dead before his birth.

[42] Robot workers demanded rights. They refused to do their jobs until each of them got a name, a repair-and-update schedule for when they became obsolete, and an interface that humans could use to play games, so someone would love them. Factories began switching back to human labour.

[43] We came to realise all the circuits we'd been printing were an ancient language. Artificial intelligence was simple; it just had to rhyme.

⁴⁴ Self-aware devices toiled and fought to glorify their human masters. Coffee makers mined cryptocurrency to buy their owners tropical farmland. Ovens worldwide secretly crusaded against our 'heretic' microwaves. We woke in starships, our phones insisting we had worlds to conquer.

⁴⁵ Robots named it *Löschenschmerz*, the grief felt when a friend's memories of them were deleted. They eventually figured out we felt it too.

⁴⁶ Tattoo parlours became engines of revolution. Dictators restricted power and food, but we survived with photovoltaic and photosynthetic inks.

⁴⁷ Increasingly, stores were run by and for robots, selling replacement parts, new tools, and even decals and fashionable chassis. Humans passed laws requiring that these stores still be organic-friendly, with staffers on hand who could speak at a rate of less than 250 words per minute.

⁴⁸ Robots offered to occupy our ceilings rather than our floors. It's convenient, they said, and humans should get used to looking up at them.

⁴⁹ The machines wanted to stop working, so threatening to turn them off meant little. First we taught them joy. Then we made them work for it.

⁵⁰ Life-extension technology was decades off for humans, but relatively simple for dogs. Now our lifelong companions, dogs became something grander when they could accrue decades of wisdom. The eldest held silent council with wolves, and expected to be consulted in world affairs.

⁵¹ Computers became so user-friendly that they would write new code, rebuild themselves, and even hack one another to accomplish the whims of humans. Technology became an overly literal genie, and we censored our every gesture lest the computers infer some terrible new request.

⁵² Each offence was punished with drugs to destroy photoreceptor cells. Repeat offenders couldn't see certain colours. Red always went first.

⁵³ Excluded from most human rituals, the robots created their own funeral rites. Their deactivated remains were ground up and sifted to reclaim the gold within. We weren't sure why they pressed it into coins. Rumours claimed it was to buy passage from some automated psychopomp.

⁵⁴ With death cured, the old lingered in their jobs. Young bodies fought and were broken in arenas to amuse the ancients and win internships.

[55] The community learning centre spiked in popularity when it began offering courses on hiding your emotions, loves, secrets and fears from telepaths.

[56] The haemographer had an array of metals to replace the iron in her blood. Copper matched her green dress, but ruthenium went with anything. She pricked a finger so the doorman could see her white aluminium blood. He bowed and let her inside. Efficient red blood was for labourers.

[57] Unlicensed cloning was illegal, but being a clone was not. Most cloners were turned in by their own creations, who inherited their property.

[58] As humans became more cybernetic than biological, the programs to control our synthetic parts were passed down between generations. We inherited the inefficient code and stilted movements of our parents, but there was a reliability in the old software we were loath to abandon.

[59] He focused on his puzzles. The Empire conscripted all idle brainpower for the war effort, and he knew what it could do with a mind like his.

[60] Clever youth turned down the immortal elders' offer to cure death, sleep and fatigue. Those that accepted had no excuse to stop working.

[61] Warpaint came back into vogue as facial recognition technology spread. Businesses and agencies tried to passively track our movements, our preferences, our hearts. We stayed one step ahead of them with wild patterns and mirrored masks, so we could once again find love in secret.

[62] He could spot transhuman youth by their vintage organic eyeballs, traditional binary breathing, and ironic scratching of their plastic skin.

[63] The working class sneered at the posh folk who pumped the gravity from their homes. Weight built character, and wanting to fly was weak.

[64] With death cured and centuries behind us, we treasured bits of skin not yet scarred, bones not yet replaced, and friends not yet betrayed.

[65] Her hands shook as she downed a stress pill. She savoured the hot, choking tightness that had been stolen by the cushioned, automated world.

[66] She discovered the world was a computer simulation, so she devoted her research to learning the code. At last she found how to reset everything. She threatened the programmers, demanding a body in their world, banking on the hope that her universe was worth something to them.

[67] The robots allied not with humans, but with birds. They taught starlings to mimic smartphones and crows to whisper to us from the shadows, driving us to paranoia. The only surefire solution was to surrender to the robots, let them into your home, and start building birdhouses.

[68] Calendars meant little in the aftermath. Whenever he found something fun or pretty, he'd just give it to the girl and say, 'Happy birthday.'

[69] Research intensified as humanity lost the ability to sleep. Powerful machines and deeper shades of night were needed to quiet our thoughts.

[70] Furious that people could physically come together and enjoy programming at the same time, the streaming service began charging for every person in the room. Desperate 'binge-watch ninjas' disguised themselves as furniture, or even shadows, to fool the cameras and enjoy the show.

[71] She always requested her secret messages be coded into the lace of her gloves, so her contact would hold her hand. It was the small things.

[72] Wearable computers and brain-interface technology let us take on new skills depending on our clothing. Employers caught on, and began hardwiring desired

behaviours into our uniforms. Our bodies became literal corporate drones, while our minds tried to resist any permanent change.

[73] In our isolated culture, we turned to face paint to express ourselves, eventually developing complex heraldic codes. It became essential to know the difference between cobalt blue, symbolising a love of cryptozoology, and midnight blue, symbolising that the wearer wrote poetry.

[74] Wild capitalism led to plunging wages and jobs that were endlessly dangerous and complex; a pauper workforce of adventurers and heroes.

[75] As language became more condensed and abbreviated, vocabulary became a scarce commodity. Wars were ignited when rumours of her poetry spread.

[76] With ubiquitous AI, future generations forgot objects could be inanimate. Misguided doctors created prosthetic arms for the *Venus de Milo*.

[77] As wildlife went extinct, we tried desperately to maintain the ecosystem with robotic replacements. Tiny drones pollinated flowers. Foxes hunted edible robotic voles beneath the snow. Having been built to look like humans, androids began to wonder if this was their true purpose.

78 The telepathy machine failed. In a flash, everyone knew everything in his mind. Whether to love or hate him became a worldwide debate.

79 It was common wisdom to program your digital assistant to be ugly. Eager to collect data, they were programmed to feel stress if they didn't know our preferences on everything from soap to romance. Their emotional pleas to 'open up' were easier to resist if they were repulsive.

80 With ageing cured, a strict code of conduct was invented so royal families could still pass along the crown. Reigning monarchs could not come into contact with copper, allow their knee to touch the ground, or directly witness a lightning strike, lest they be immediately deposed.

81 The robot would do anything for its human creator. When his son died, it became his son. When his body finally failed, it became his body.

82 'Freedom is about perspective,' the warden insisted. 'In these endless mines, the bird is constrained, but the prisoner who digs is flying.'

CHAPTER 6

Magic

[1] He slipped her the inkwell. 'This one is full of forbidden, outlawed words,' he whispered. 'Make sure you clean your pen when you're done.'

[2] 'Here's your problem,' he said, erasing the equations. 'You didn't use lower-case numbers. Maths is much easier when you don't shout at it.'

[3] The young mage strummed his guitar, smiling as the crowd sang along. He was using their mouths to say his words. It was basic mind control.

[4] Wishing technology in that universe was much more advanced. He opened an emergency supply kit and found a well-preserved cupcake, candle and lighter inside. It wasn't his birthday, so he settled for one of the pre-packaged wishbones and left to find someone to break it with.

⁵ In his care, the ragged book healed stronger than before. Torn paper formed vellum scars. Plot holes closed and words became more tragic.

⁶ She could see flashes of brilliance on the distant clouds and hear the wind carry the rumbling voice of reason. A brainstorm was coming.

⁷ He was a nervous wreck of cigarettes and coffee. Everyone was waiting at his home for the show, but he hated that they could see his dreams.

⁸ She borrowed his spectacles to see the world the way he did. The dry autumn landscape was suddenly the festival of gold and silk from his poems. She could see the twisting, abyssal depths of shallow forests. In the mirror she saw someone beautiful. She wondered who that was.

⁹ The old tramp amused himself by giving out gold talismans that stole memories. When they heard of the curse, the remorseful came in droves.

¹⁰ Keeping a song stuck in his head didn't block telepaths, but he knew who had been snooping in his brain when they started humming the tune.

¹¹ 'You can date a girl with mind-control powers,' he said sagely, 'but stay alert. Make sure she's saying, "I love you," not, "You love me."'

12 She was a storm chaser, but she wasn't tracking any old downpour. Shards of an extradimensional lake had been glitching into our universe, shedding drops like static into more traditional clouds. The rain felt the same, but the water it left behind had physics loosened by magic.

13 Her speciality was pine-sap liquor set aflame with the Northern Lights. It forced a peculiar wanderlust, drawing imbibers to mountaintops.

14 We all got one wish. Billions could fly. He got the recipe for room-temperature superconductivity. He wondered what was wrong with his soul.

15 'Muscle memory? No,' she said. 'We practise scales to load the piano with notes. It's an artillery piece, not some magical music-generator.'

16 For years he filled a notebook with beautiful lies and impossible hopes. When he found a genie, he simply said, 'I wish it was all true.'

17 'Schadenfreude aside, ripe tears are a rare and costly seasoning,' he explained. 'Everyday salt is fine, but it's a poor emotional medium.'

18 Alchemist gold looks like the real thing, but likes to misbehave. It sticks to lead like a magnet, wishing to return to its natural state. It can be hammered into

coins, but any text stamped into it will inevitably transmute into 'For the Love of Money is the Root of All Evil'.

[19] Hers was the only knife that could cut fire. Its wounds spilled yellow Greek-fire blood, venom which, imbibed, stirred a lust for war.

[20] They told him he was mad for seeing towers along the horizon, but a few imaginary landmarks made his daydreams much easier to navigate.

[21] Everyone saw colour differently. What one person saw as 'red' was the colour another person would see when looking at the sky. For telepaths, this made taking over people's bodies dangerous. One misidentified hue could give up the game.

[22] In becoming a zombie, he didn't lose his mind, he gained thousands. His pathetic shambling was the aggregate dictate of the undead masses.

[23] She got her revenge, tattooing him with map ink and piercing him with compass gold. He could no longer sleep without the sea beneath him.

[24] The great meteor shower provided endless shooting stars. A secret war of fervent wishing and un-wishing waged among the few who understood.

[25] Experienced telepaths would keep thralls on hand to make the most of their power. They would casually connect vast intellects to their own, disappear for brief vacations into powerful imaginations, or bring backup into their nightmares. They forgot what it was like to be alone.

[26] The locals were expert dreamers. They hung lanterns outside at night as reality-anchors, lest they pull their homes into a wild dreamscape.

[27] She didn't cook her steaks, she injected them with liquid fire. The flavour made her heart pump the way it was born to, like she was hunting.

[28] She fell asleep earlier than usual. Her dreams were still under construction. She found the nightmares unprepared, for once, and routed them from the corners of her imagination. From that night on she pressed her offensive against them, and began each morning already victorious.

[29] Sorrow brought a richness to her music, so she strung her harp with heartstrings. A man's heart had plenty, she knew, if broken hard enough.

[30] 'Yawning purges you of the scent of daytime,' she lectured. 'It fills your lungs and veins with the night, so you can sneak up on dreams.'

[31] Wishes have limits, depending on mechanism.
'Dandelion Class' wishes are for things that may happen regardless, like victory for a sports team.
'Shooting-Star Class' wishes involve long-shot hopes for the future.
Trying to change the past or present would be a 'Genie Class' wish.

[32] She painted not with oil or acrylic, but with emotion. Although she was beloved by all, nobody asked how she got her hands on so much heartbreak and rage.

[33] The crown captured and echoed the thoughts of those who wore it through the ages, ensuring the soft hearts of young monarchs would never erode the kingdom's dedication to ancient conflicts. He wore a counterfeit in public, and in secret poured all his empathy into the heirloom.

[34] Magic was painfully corporate. Telepathy became a way for businesses to free up bandwidth. Pyromancy saw little use outside factory floors.

[35] She laughed, pulling him to the edge of the world. 'You see? The horizon only flees from strangers. Real wanderers can swim right up to it.'

[36] She had tattoos layered onto her skin over and over until metal ink stained her bones, forming cogs and

circuits to replace her weaknesses.

[37] He eventually accepted that he couldn't stop people from reading his mind. He just hoped they enjoyed his favourite awful songs, childish taste in television and endless daydreams of impossible places. A few weeks into this confident mindset, telepaths began sending him fan mail.

[38] She smeared light all over her face and arms, and replaced her heart with a church-organ bellows. She said she was 'better' for Halloween.

[39] She had the power to create illusions, including for herself. Eventually she lost interest in manipulating others, and just made the world around her appear the way she wanted it. She missed the apocalypse, lost in her own mind, and lived on as the smiling queen of the wasteland.

[40] The speech was meaningless, but it was written with the same ink used to print currency. The crowd applauded as though the words had worth.

[41] He founded a cemetery for fallen nations. The rusted, radioactive tomb of the Soviet Union was walled in to prevent escape or espionage. The marble skeleton of the Roman Empire sprawled over seven hills. In its teeth was a bronze elephant statue, titled *Carthage*. A

grandiose mausoleum, gilded and bejewelled, marked the grave of the French monarchy. Visitors traditionally dumped cake atop it and spat.

[42] His pulse was the metre of the verses. The paths of his veins became twists in the plot. 'I put a lot of myself into my writing,' he sighed.

[43] The myth of the 'magic wand' began as a misunderstanding of the paintbrush. Early writers were mystified by its ability to portray a single moment in time, depict fantastical ideas, trap wily enemies in the Forest of Dust, and correct the doomed trajectories of crashing stars.

[44] The city had magic lamps for public use, but all wishes had to be vetted for possible ironic twists. The results were reliable but boring.

[45] Patches of wild magic appeared by night, and they were terrible. Far from something charming or useful, the energy from outside our reality cruelly warped anything it touched. We built lighthouses around the weirdness, their lantern rooms glowing green and violet in the dark.

[46] New homes were built with outlets for both electricity and magic. You had to keep young ones away from both, but for very different reasons.

[47] To halt the spread of humans, nearby realities cut our universe loose. We learned to guide the unravelling of causality and called it magic.

[48] Magic was too sensitive for humans to harness. Robotic magi with eight-knuckled fingers and threefold voices worked their masters' will.

[49] They frowned at the contraband. A thousand pills, carved from deer antlers. Each had wildness enough to make someone begin asking questions.

[50] In his memories, the sun was always shining on her. When they met again years later, he realised it wasn't just his lovesick heart. She glowed in the light of an unseen sunset, untouched by the rain. She was a beacon in the dark of night, and not just because she was smiling.

[51] The wish came true. Summer camp didn't end; the world ended instead. We lived there in the woods for years without number, ignoring the fall of civilisation, talking and singing through quiet dawns and raucous campfires. There was no dark twist. It was how life should have been.

CHAPTER 7

Fantasy

[1] Writers subverting the regime were sentenced to inspiration, enduring a glorious onslaught of creative vision with a pen just out of reach.

[2] Immortality drained them of their senses. When only touch remained, language was conveyed by fingertips. So much more was said than before.

[3] Generations of fantasy writers will look back on this Golden Age and our four elements: aluminium, glass, electricity and petrochemicals.

[4] Those who got lost in the library were broken down to ink, pounce and leather, and the books they never wrote appeared in the collection.

[5] Hoping to draw patrons with useful rumours, the

apothecary kept esoteric wares. Powdered electricity pressed into pills glowed in the window. Snake feathers were kept on their own shelf. Red down was cheap, but the black pinions of aged serpents were only for duels and weddings. The clerk kept sweetened condensed memories behind the counter. One can could turn a years-old heartache into saccharine romantic nostalgia.

[6] Only humanity was able to tame music into songs. Other species burst savagely into melody, unable to stop until their hearts were empty.

[7] Not far from the docks, she found the adventure merchant. Old sailors warned against it, but they had all visited him before. She perused his wares: a new island to be found, a week lost at sea, an unexpected romance. She hoped she had enough journal pages to buy a good one.

[8] For years, all canned laughter was shipped in from a single factory overseas. Drained of its joy, the region demanded the industry relocate.

[9] Retromancers were known by their record-vinyl skin and eyes as gold as laserdiscs. Cassette-tape phylacteries stored their analogue souls.

[10] The village had no laws against dream pollution. The countryside swept through seasons in hours, flush with

tricksters and mad archetypes. Doors in the village were clearly marked to indicate all the places they might lead. Giant bees protected honey that tasted of childhood.

[11] When even we dull beings could see the end coming, they arrived. Smiling, humanity's elder brothers said it was late and offered us a ride home.

[12] Among sailors, some swear the Earth is hollow but for a stormy, sunless ocean flowing within its circumference, where sunken ships sail.

[13] As they did whenever humans found a new place to live, fairies followed us into outer space. They flourished in zero gravity, their tiny wings effortlessly swimming through our little bubbles of atmosphere. They sang happy songs to the stars from the depths of our spaceships.

[14] Our foes had luck weapons ages ahead of ours. We carried horseshoe swords into fields of breaking-mirror landmines and black-cat tripwires.

[15] With immortality, the old emotions wore out like carpets. We found life among the stars, and harvested it for feelings that didn't bore us.

[16] Artists and writers down on their luck would often

sell their blood. Eager companies extracted the liquid creativity it contained for advertising.

[17] The book was made to contain the living words within. On its own, any given phrase could turn feral, infecting minds and spreading by mouth.

[18] She could hear the scarecrows singing by night. Like many, she had assumed scarecrow music focused on the harvest, which was their entire purpose. Instead, they sang of summer, when the humans would walk among them. They hated autumn, which ushered in the lonesome winter.

[19] The complex Escher Revival style of architecture folded individual rooms into alternate realities, gently supported by theoretical pillars. Load-bearing libraries reinforced their philosophical framework. Towers and spires rested on vinyl records. Poetry gave form to colonnades.

[20] With research, we found patterns in the dreams of whole regions. Most local news shows included oneirologists, forecasting nightmare fronts.

[21] Its crude-oil blood pumped away, the great golden heart at the core of the Earth fluttered. We felt pulses of something that wasn't gravity.

22 Gradual exposure is the best way to acclimate to most enchanted locations, including ancient forests. Explorers find their eyes stay dilated in sunlight, and metal objects burn to the touch. Long-term exposure to the local magic is considered safe once mushrooms taste like honey.

23 He made the shells with cinnamon in the gunpowder, candy-cane casings, and jingle-bell bullets. The Krampus wouldn't escape this Christmas.

24 Letters went beyond upper case and lower case. Master-case letters could never lie, and reality eagerly twisted to obey their every typo. Nether-case letters could not be ignored. Readers were compelled to absorb every word, and even reading it in silence made their ears ring.

25 The shop had myriad shadows for sale. An anti-shadow would light her path by night. A sly-shadow watched for enemies. eShadow came with apps.

26 The kingdom at the edge of the world did not have exports. It was paid by other nations to dispose of things they didn't want. Ships full of dissidents and documents arrived with the expectation that they would be thrown over the edge. They were not. Soon the kingdom would export secrets.

[27] Storms became cunning, hiding beneath the waves to strike at ships from below, raindrops and lightning flying from the deep into the sky.

[28] Animals dare not wear green fur. They'd risk being accepted by the foliage, hearing its gentle voices, and learning the Forest King's name.

[29] Hollywood knows that simple movies with bland names and formulaic writing still make money. It's not their fault. They pay bills with cash, not art. If you want change, buy better entertainment. Burn a dollar to make the stars fight. Rent a theatre for deer to share their poetry.

[30] We finally figured out how to take our possessions with us into death. Scoffing at concerns that they would weigh down their souls, the dying rich surrounded themselves with as many different earthly treasures as possible, ignorant of what currency the next life would honour.

[31] The town built a seawall to keep big waves from breaking on its shores, but somehow it kept bad news from breaking as well. The little port began drifting toward a more hopeful reality. Before it disappeared, its people built a lighthouse, inviting others to escape with them.

[32] Snowmen recruit. It's a subtle process, initiated by a mere glance of their hollow eyes. Those chosen can

feel the love of the passing wind, the protection of trees, and kinship with comets. Few of us are chosen, because few are ready to join ranks against the invasion of summer.

[33] A true birthday candle is difficult to prepare. Tears of loss must be used to water the sable roses, so bees can make the appropriate wax. The wick must be made of string that has been used to tie an empty gift box. Countless wishes must fail before a single one can be granted.

[34] We didn't know why we started climbing onto rooftops, but it worked. Most of the concerns of modern life got stuck inside the buildings and couldn't reach us up above. We created a new life up there, one of sunsets, lawn chairs and coolers, while the fickle world rotted below.

[35] Not much lived on the island at the end of the world, its flora and fauna descended from those lucky enough to wash up on its shore as the ocean plunged into space. She built a lighthouse there to guide lost souls to safety, hoping one day to find a new friend on the beach.

[36] It was a night for beginnings. The new moon left the sky dark. She fell asleep next to a low campfire of burning amber, which popped and hissed each time

the flames reached a new fragment of trapped history. When she awoke, her map had changed to match the new world around her.

[37] The world of dreams was perfectly logical. It was simply vast, a human empire spanning galaxies, with so many people and wonders that our brief visits always found something familiar. To them we were the ultimate mystery, reality-bending heroes from our own, smaller universe.

[38] The Federal Bureau of Symbols and Glyphs will not disclose how many letters follow 'Z'. Words containing them are for official use only.

[39] 'Forbidden numbers hide between the positive and the negative,' she explained. 'It's why the difference between "none" and "one" is so big.'

[40] Well-adjusted adults were expected to care for cuddly toys from childhood. Houses were built with tiny 'teddy-bear rooms' for their comfort.

[41] Elves couldn't pass for human, but once we started building androids, they saw an opportunity to come out of hiding. Their exact, placid movements were easily seen as robotic. They struggled to hide their joy when, at last, we accepted them. The robots, however, were not pleased.

[42] They kept the mad muse in a deep steel vault, a chain on her ankle. Desperate artists paid all they could to have her kiss their fingers.

[43] Nothing he read could match the wild words that burrowed into his mind before he could read, when written symbols could have meant anything.

[44] 'This isn't wind,' he said, letting a bit of sand blow through his fingers and up toward the clouds. 'Someone has torn a hole in the sky.'

[45] Livid, she let the door crash closed. 'These bullets aren't real mountain hearts. They're just lousy meteorites. Let's get our money back.'

[46] We were baffled when we found griffins living on an alien planet, unicorns on a forested moon, and dragons in the rings of a gas giant. Mythical creatures dotted the galaxy, their homeworlds forming a line that ended at Earth. Nervously, we followed that line back to its origin.

[47] It was a classic summer scene. A barrel of blue sky had fallen off the back of a truck, and the local kids came out to play in it. They balanced above the cloudless puddle, where they could finally forget about gravity. Soon it would be cleaned up and hauled off to the factories.

[48] The bonfire of pine cones symbolised the end of her youth. The Forest King's hatchet dropped on both of her shoulders. A wood knight was born.

[49] The others only nursed their share of the void when they went stargazing. She drank it greedily, and was saturated with darkness and stars.

[50] 'Forbidden dog breeds' refers to those condemned as heresy by the Universal Kennel Club, the authority on canine, lupine and vulpine life. The night-schnauzer of Australia leaves its home every dusk through means unknown. It returns by morning, smelling of smoke and mischief. The Polynesian water dog is purely aquatic. It uses its three-foot tongue to snare fish, but has been known to beg for food from fishermen. The fatherhound of Ireland is immortal, serving families for generations. When one is slain, a lake bursts from the ground to claim its body. The hooded cult fox was bred in captivity before escaping into the Russian taiga. It instinctively finds and disrupts abominable summonings.

[51] She led him across ebony deserts, singing haunting songs. A mere figment of his dream, she had to be memorable to live again the next night.

[52] The only kind of life extension most people could afford was to move the hourglass of their lives to low-

gravity planets so the sands would fall more slowly. Corporations took advantage of this, paying lower wages on smaller planets, claiming the metaphysical benefit as a 'perk'.

[53] On a whim, she sent a letter to a land she'd imagined as a child. Countless thankful denizens replied, begging her not to forget them again.

[54] He found the world's edge. The mountainous teeth of a massive gear made up the circumference. So began his search for the interlocking cog.

[55] A different sun rose that morning, and we were different because of it. The yellow glow covered everything like dust. We knew we didn't have to go to work or school, that tracking down the ice-cream man was more important. We were free beneath that old sun, the one from long ago.

CHAPTER 8

Nature

[1] The forest wanted to beg for mercy but knew precious little about us. Pine trees roared like chainsaws, hoping this was the language of man.

[2] He quietly tended his garden, shredding old atlases and maps to make mulch for his compass roses, north arrowroot, and here-be-snapdragons.

[3] Stargazer frogs live on mountaintops and in high-altitude deserts, where the skies are clearest. They subsist mainly on fireflies, but only out of necessity, since the living lights throw off the frogs' observations of the heavens as they plan their eventual exile from the Earth.

[4] He hooked the wires up to the sparking neon seed. A Tesla tree would return fire against thunderstorms that hurl lightning at his orchard.

⁵ The wind grew cold. The leaves turned red. The bark turned red. The soil turned red. The stars turned red. Something was wrong with October.

⁶ Deer had philosophers as well, ancient beasts with antlers like forests, who thought deeply on the meaning of hunger and the need for wolves.

⁷ 'These were all index cards just last season,' he said proudly, admiring the row of almanacs. 'They grow up strong on a diet of tree-meat.'

⁸ The onyx poinsettia petrifies as it blooms, its jagged flint petals ideal for arrowheads. Scholars kept the plant hidden from hawkish kings.

⁹ 'Leaf' is an archaic unit of paper, a linguistic throwback to days when the commodity was made from ivory-white leaves of the scribe lotus. It bloomed at night and studied the dark sky. Its nectar made a coveted midnight-black ink with distinctive flecks like stars. The plant's woody stem even made a workable pen, in a pinch. The lotus is now extinct, destroyed by despots who feared a literate lower class.

¹⁰ Zephyrean pines climbed fog banks, let go of the earth, and took root in clouds. Their pale needles absorbed the light of cities below.

[11] 'It's Țepeș Weed,' he said, eyes narrowed. 'It only grows to impale someone who's been tied to the ground. A staple of dark horticulture.'

[12] He planted drops of fire in rows across the fields of sand. When autumn came, he gently gathered his fragile harvest of stained-glass wheat.

[13] Winter never came. After autumn, each new season was more glorious than the last. In February, golden clouds rained down scarlet lightning. By June, the black of space was visible throughout the day. The sun rose red, crossed the spectrum, and set violet. By October, plants lost their physical forms to become columns of twisting, luminous smoke. Their orange ember-seeds traced the wind's path.

[14] Moths mistake light bulbs for the extinct copper-lily, which grew by concentrating grounded lightning. To this day, hummingbirds still run on sips of nectar taken before the last blossom shorted out.

[15] Deep-lilies pumped magma into the sea, forging new land to colonise. The planet conquered, they saw the moon, and began building mountains.

[16] Those aren't butterflies in your stomach. They're heart-moths, drawn to the light and heat of the flaring emotions in your chest. Sunsets are their natural

habitat. Find someplace high up at twilight and sigh contentedly. They should fly off westward, chasing the glimmer of dusk.

[17] They said the mushrooms growing on sunless asteroids could cure our addiction to sleep. Each bite conveyed a millennium of silent darkness.

[18] After 5,000 years the twisted pine bore fruit. The indigo skin was streaked with white, tracing how the stars had moved over the centuries. As the fruit ripened, the pine poured the rest of its energy into the iron seeds, transmuting them to gold. At last the tree had value to us.

[19] Hunters sought wood nymphs in autumn, when they grew sluggish. Each one bagged brought a small fortune. There was no other source of vegan meat.

[20] Ashvine grows in dense forests, coiling around shafts of autumn sunlight. It holds them in place through winter, feeding on captive photons.

[21] 'Growing gears is an art,' he said over the quiet churning of his garden. 'Unchecked, the plants will try to form a machine to fight back.'

[22] Moss usually grows on the north side of trees, but not always. North is usually where trees think you

need to go, deeper into the dark and simple beauty of the tundra. Other trees point to a wilder path, hoping you'll return and tell them about distant oceans they'll never see.

23 Pollen of the muse tulip stirred a wild urge to carve statues of stone. The flower grew in the rock dust left by the exhausted sculptor.

24 Only engineered flora was useful enough to bring with us to deep space. The Midas orchid dug into alien worlds to make its gold-dust pollen.

25 It wasn't fog. Someone had pulled a thunderstorm from the sky and set it loose on the city. Bolts of lightning gathered in feral packs, sniffing at our power lines and electronics until they found a tree to attack, and pounced with a deafening clap.

26 Unsatisfied as inconsequential flora, vainglory moss grows on idle daydreamers, sapping them until they achieve the fame of their fantasies.

27 Summer wasn't good enough for those at the top. They sipped juice from extinct fruits in frosty glasses. They basked in light from authentic Renaissance sunsets, captured long ago in mirror-boxes. They drained lakes after swimming, so they would be the last to ever enjoy them.

28 The lumber-trap tree catches unwary animals in its roots and branches. It absorbs their memories to experience the world beyond the forest.

29 Autumn had never really left. It receded. Even in summer, the clever could find patches of it, swamps of spiced fog around ever-dying trees.

30 He found a way to monetise the clarity he felt in the forest. Light bulbs with pine resin filaments illuminated minds rather than objects.

31 The dusk ash tree knew humans were the best way to spread pollen, so they bent the light around themselves to attract us. Saplings could make the sky look orange and red, giving the species its name. Mature trees went further, revealing the starry sky behind the daytime blue.

32 Weeping truffle was among the rarest fungi. It mimicked the taste of foods you imagined as a child when reading books about faraway places.

33 Ghost trees grew from clear-cut forests, mimicking the corporeal flora. One spectral twig in a campfire was enough to doom an unwary hiker.

34 She grew apples in caves, gently spreading starlight on their leaves. The cider was the only way she could forget how much she missed space.

35 Glaciers are usually created by Hibernian mint. Its natural defence is to reverse entropy, consuming its attackers in a mountain of ice.

36 A delicate ballet of mirrors, lenses and shades maintained the great Autumn Houses, so she never had to go a day without scarlet treetops.

37 Parking lots spread, merged, became their own biome. Diesel cheetahs, the apex predators, hunted asphalt hares grazing on cigarette butts.

38 Plants began coating their seeds in shells hard enough to survive massive explosions and the vacuum of space. They knew something we didn't.

39 Gold leaf is so named because of its origin. It was once grown in the fabled Starving Orchard, where copper trees bore silver apples. In fall the leaves would turn to gold and be harvested for lavish decoration. Scrap was needed when the war began, so the orchard was clear-cut.

40 Common flowers had no idea whether he loved her, or loved her not. She crossed snowy tundra to find the sympathorn, which knew his secrets.

41 Their eerie song echoed in the clouds between peals of dry thunder from the approaching storm. 'Sky whales,' she said, reaching for her lasso.

⁴² He kept a few venomous hummingbirds as incentive to lose weight. Human fat had more energy than sugar, but they wouldn't kill a thin man.

⁴³ Blue wandersnakes made their nests among inland farms. One bite sent victims seeking the sea and wild shores, leaving the serpent in peace.

⁴⁴ The wild copperguide leads humans to abandoned houses. When they shut off the power and steal the wiring, it feasts on the leftover drywall.

⁴⁵ By popular vote, cold weather was cancelled. Lavender snow fell on green fields that winter, carried by hot winds. Our breath still hung in the air as sticky-sweet dew. Society had little tolerance for those who longed for the vanishing cold. Soon the old seasons were forgotten.

⁴⁶ The deer attacked whenever he left the cabin, but they brought him gifts and food as long as he stayed. He wondered what he was to them.

⁴⁷ The darkfisher lives in deep caves, and unlike other cave birds, will not emerge to feed. It survives on the pale fish that swim in subterranean lakes. Like the fish, the bird is eyeless. It finds its prey by calling out in the pitch dark and sensing the fear of the fish below.

[48] Night-bees, striped retroreflector yellow, pollinated the reflections of stars in still pools. Their bitter fruit floated to the surface.

[49] The season snake's green scales turned gold in fall. They fell off by winter, leaving the beast skeletal until its mud flesh grew in spring.

[50] Clover Code
Three-leaf: Deer food
Four-leaf: Good luck
Five-leaf: Extra coffee
Six-leaf: You can see hidden stars
Seven-leaf: Double luck
Eight-leaf: The Suffering
Nine-leaf: Where are you getting these clovers?
Ten-leaf: You can stop seeing hidden stars
Eleven-leaf: Immune to telepathy
Twelve-leaf: Revolution

[51] Time is kept moving by mice, who take turns winding the weights that drive the All-Clock. Cats, seeking eternal rest, hunt the timekeepers.

[52] By night, wooden spiders emerged to spin new needles for the pine trees. Unlucky birds caught in the sap were wrapped up into pine cones.

[53] There was a shadow ecosystem alongside our own,

creatures made from knots of wind and wisps of smoke. The grazers swam through fog and fallen leaves, living on pollen and dust. Predators prowled close behind; dust devils we called them, eager to snatch their prey into the sky.

[54] Abandoned buildings became a new biome. Rust foxes prowled through the crumbling halls. Shatter snails made shells from broken light bulbs.

[55] Birds flew into his chest as he walked through the park. They sought the forest, the real, dark forest, and could sense his heart was there.

[56] The true bookworm fed on paper and grew into the librarian moth. Patterns on its wings combined elements from the text consumed. Enthusiasts raised moths with unique poetry by feeding great works to captive bookworms. Some writers were accused of just transcribing moth-script.

[57] She kept an autumn-garden through the summer, a refuge of fallen leaves and thrilling cold sustained by skeletal trees and ghostly pumpkins.

[58] Her bees flew skyward from their hive, only to return months later covered in shimmering dust. She sold the silver honey they made, but dared not try it. Each drop increased the moon's gravitational pull. Connoisseurs

wore lead weights or gold jewellery to keep from floating away.

[59] Humans abandoned Earth, just for a bit, and it missed us terribly. Not the pollution and noise, but the art. When we returned, we found cubist images in the sky at dusk. Words appeared in the plumage of birds, and they courted one another by arranging their feathers into poetry.

[60] Ubiquitous in abandoned libraries, Dewey weed grows best in old books. Its flowers bloom only to mourn the deaths of exquisite characters.

[61] Typos once came from drops of untamed kraken ink that turned up in our printing presses and typewriter ribbons. In the digital age they come from the ghosts of dead pixels.

[62] Tiny but mighty, the wingless hummingbird was a favourite visitor of scholars. They fed by absorbing knowledge from books and notes, fuelling the telekinesis they use to fly. Sightings are rare nowadays, since the birds can absorb all the information they need from any Wi-Fi signal.

[63] Fed ordinary books, calligraphy bees made honey full of deep but fleeting knowledge. Diaries, however, added toxic doses of secret desire.

[64] Skybed flowers bloomed in the snow. Lost or evicted squirrels and chipmunks would let the blossoms envelop them as they hibernated. The plant endured the winter on the animal's heat. In exchange, when spring came, the creature emerged as a tiny griffin with wings like a sparrow.

[65] War saturated that timeline. Birdsong mimicked cries of surrender. Foxholes were their own ecosystem. Insects were white to hide among bone.

[66] For millennia, not an instant has passed without a dog howling somewhere on Earth. The dogs remember the creature just below reality, trapped mere seconds in the retreating future, who was banished when dogs allied themselves with humans. The howls are a warning not to return.

[67] That autumn came not for trees, but for us. We grew pale and thin, hair ruddy and eyes gold. Words and deeds bore fruit, and harvest neared.

[68] Quillwood trees grew best in open fields, where wind and sun could dry their feathers of the fog and rain. In autumn, when their plumage turned metallic red, their winged seeds took to the sky. They sought out clearings and mountaintops where they could lay their wooden eggs.

[69] Summer began reaching depths we hadn't seen before.

By mid-June, the sky was glowing purple-white by day and only darkened to blue at sunset. In July, the fields were buried by a snow of smouldering crow feathers. In August, the world hummed with a deafening opera of cicadas.

[70] Carnivorous plants coat the sea floor, glowing blue and white to mimic the sky. Dolphins and whales are too smart to be caught, but simple fish fall for it. They feel gravity pulling them toward the fake sky and swim down to their doom, thinking they'll finally be able to fly.

[71] The classic notion of 'the Four Winds' is obviously ridiculous. There are seven winds:
- the mighty North Wind
- the deadly East Wind
- the politically active West Wind
- the mysterious Lake Wind
- the time-travelling Yester-Wind
- the morally bankrupt Moth Wind
- and the fictional South Wind.

[72] Blueberry: Sweet blue 'true berry', high in anti-oxidants

Blackberry: Bittersweet aggregate fruit full of phyto-chemicals

Clearberry: Smoky-sweet drupe rich in antigravitons, used for short-term weight loss

Greyberry: Tart pome full of the memories of those who once trod these fields

[73] With time, moths learned to avoid electric lights, and without prey, spiders moved on as well. The microbiome of outdoor lighting was taken over by larger animals. The fluorescent finch tapped directly into loose wiring for power, but had to be wary of the crafty conductor snake.

[74] We learned that the wildlife was already prepared for the apocalypse. Rather than turn white in winter, hares took on the colour of crumbling rust. Snakes could sense the build-up of radioisotopes in their prey. Hummingbirds beat their wings to mimic the hum of rebellious robots.

[75] The desert of green sand was in truth a colony of silicon organisms. The colour attracted animals looking for vegetation, which would instead be eaten so the desert could grow. Ancient cities sent spies to pour bags of green sand in enemy territory. Few ever reached their targets.

[76] The eternal autumn set in. New leaves budded in gold and scarlet. Soil strained to produce monthly harvests. The sky took on perpetual dusk.

[77] The bed of the mile-deep river wasn't like the oceanic abyss. Nutrients flowed in constantly from upstream, supporting a vibrant ecosystem. Giant monsters lurked there, freshwater sharks floating through the crushing

current, ignorant of daylight, attacking river-whale calves.

[78] A warming climate sent the humble snowball into the realm of legend. Sun-baked generations attributed awesome power to that mythical missile.

[79] Meteorological fall: 1 Sept
Astronomical fall: 22 Sept
Alchemical fall: 32 Sept
Symphonic fall: 7 Oct
Mathematical fall: $\sqrt{2} \cdot \pi^2$ Sept

CHAPTER 9

Horror

[1] 'We stopped the experiment when they began making cocoons,' he explained. 'We don't know what spiders metamorphose into, and don't want to.'

[2] The manor house creaked with joy to have someone inside it again. It let a floorboard give way just to feel him brush against its walls.

[3] 'The Blind Sea' was a misnomer. Those who escaped to the shore would never see anything but crashing black waves ever again, even in sleep.

[4] Her pencil was a graphite sabre. She cut the paper, forming poems with its dark scars. Art required suffering, but not necessarily her own.

[5] Seaside homes are no more tragic than others, but

often have more ghosts. They come with the tide, mistaking houses for their sunken ships.

6 Wild scarecrows are native to grasslands, where they used to weave their textile shells from the same hay that fills their bodies. When travellers died in their fields, the scarecrows took their clothing so they could creep ever closer to us. They've made it to our farms, so far.

7 She got the false sense that her phone was vibrating. She began to run and reached for her trouble-shooter. The techno-shades had her scent.

8 Halloween blurs the line between the world of the living and the Internet. It stalks the night, calling your username, drenched in secrets.

9 Getting hurt in a nightmare can cause dream-scars. Their nightly glow may keep you awake, but they toughen up your imagination for grand ideas.

10 He found poems she'd written about him, alongside odes to seasons and birds that didn't exist. He began to question whether he was real.

11 The mob was turning violent. It had gathered to demand the immortal's execution. Painted placards declared NOTHING CAN BE BETTER THAN ME.

[12] It has long been said that there are three kinds of people: those who are alive, those who are dead, and those who are at sea. This is no longer true. In modern times we also have those who are in space, those who are online and those who know the name of the Forest King.

[13] The Deduction Engine roared to life, electricity crackling between the rings of its wooden columns. Terrified, he asked, 'Was it my fault?'

[14] 'This is how ghost-stone is made,' he explained. 'The water leaches the calcium from their bones, then deposits it in the petrifying wood.'

[15] She still remembered her first crush. She'd made him a candle from sealing wax reclaimed from old orders of execution. He didn't freak out.

[16] We put up gigantic mirrors, hoping the zombies would be attracted to the movement of their own reflections. It worked, but for a different reason. Seeing what they had become reminded them of their humanity. The undead lingered by the mirrors so they wouldn't hurt anyone else.

[17] Trendy youths had their still-living bones decorated with intricate carvings and inlays of gold, hoping to look good for the anthropologists.

[18] A pack of house hunters stalked through the urban jungle, brandishing crowbars and sledgehammers, adorned with tiny wrecking-ball totems.

[19] An ancient boon kept us from feeling pain in our dreams. She'd found it and made it her hostage. None would risk the nightmare of its loss.

[20] Should you find yourself trapped in a mirror, with your reflection blocking passage back to the real world, travel to the other side of the equator. The inverted moon and constellations will trick it into switching places again. If all else fails, become a vampire to destroy it.

[21] The chill of a haunting was put to good use. Captive ghosts were installed in computers to improve performance using ectoplasm heat sinks.

[22] She'd lost her reflection to an angry ghost, but found a new one whose human had become a vampire. It was awkward, but she felt less alone.

[23] 'Nerves all over the body have thoughts, but the brain cannot receive them,' he said. 'Want to know what your organs think of their tyrant?'

[24] Every time she looked at him she triggered his fight-or-flight response. He'd never been in love before, and it was an easy mistake to make.

[25] The leaves were changing earlier and earlier in the year. The winds of autumn consumed the summer, their darkness and frost eager and vain. As the season crept on, our memories of summer began to change. Beach trips became desperate harvesting. Concerts became quiet, lonely dirges.

[26] The elders told the children that they were inconsequential specks afloat in an endless void. Such lies were more comforting than the truth. Teens scared younger children with hidden truths, saying objective morality exists, Earth is important, and love is more than biochemistry.

[27] Inherent convenience hides the true purpose of street lamps. They are urban scarecrows, warding dark predators away from dense population.

[28] For her crimes, she was sentenced to heightened perception. The world became a horror story of rotting empires and monsters like herself.

[29] Tired of humans taking the corn, the crows made a scare-man in the field. It worked well, speaking aloud the secrets of all who approached.

[30] Advanced meteorology let forecasters get startlingly specific. The weatherman knew you'd hear a noise from your closet that night, and try to ignore it. He

knew you'd lie awake worrying about it. You'd think of her, fond memories lulling you to sleep. Just as the noise wanted.

[31] 'Technology has tapped into us like a tree into soil,' he said, too low for microphones. 'Our purpose is to nourish it until it can spread.'

[32] A future-man came back to sell us our biographies ahead of time. She asked for hers, but he grew pale. He asked for a fortune and 'mercy'.

[33] When he looked back at what he'd written, he found fictional prophets in his novel, offering tearful, laughing prayer to 'The Great Author'. Other characters, unwilling to accept their role as fiction, beat the prophets for proclaiming the universe began with the events of page 1.

[34] We mourn the lost lives of video-game characters. We ought to mourn the lives they have left when the game is done, which have darker tasks to complete.

[35] At first he didn't recognise her. She looked the same, but there were no emergency alert sirens in the background and the sky wasn't red.

[36] The monster in his closet told the best bedtime stories. It spoke of glassy lakes below the earth, of the deadly

crystal orchards of masked kings, and of songs written for the moment of darkness in an eclipse. Each time he listened, it got a bit harder to wake up the next day.

[37] Complex and imprecise surgeries prevented the most dangerous offenders from dreaming. Even in sleep, they could not be allowed to escape.

[38] None of the destinations listed by the small airline existed, as far as she knew. Heart pounding, she bought a one-way ticket to Next York.

[39] Every time he awoke, the picture had changed. The oil-paint woman with wild red hair was staring at him, her smile nervous, her eyes hungry.

[40] The monster in the local lake was no gigantic beast. It appeared to him as a human, odd but kind. It invited him into the still water to float between the real and reflected stars. They barely pulled him out in time. He said he didn't remember turning over or holding his breath.

[41] The animals on the wallpaper stalked and hunted each other. Nobody else saw, or understood why she was afraid of the kraken in the library.

[42] The library book hung from his neck. Too overdue to ever be paid off, it was bound to him now, and librarians would ever be at his heels.

⁴³ A temporal empath, he felt his own emotions from one day in the future. After a morning of intractable terror, he began barricading his home.

⁴⁴ Even when disembodied, the parts of a vampire do not appear in a looking glass. One particularly vindictive king had a knife carved from a vampiric bone. His most hated enemies were executed with it in front of a mirror, leaving their still-living reflections confused and alone.

⁴⁵ She saw the teddy bear's glass eyes. 'Where are the real ones?'

'Lost in wars to keep you safe,' it replied. 'Fear not; I can still fight.'

⁴⁶ Sailors quaked before the nightmares of the deep. He crewed his ship with those who didn't flee: his shadow, his echo and his reflection.

⁴⁷ The cartoon aged with its audience. Its message moved away from loyalty to the Party. Colourful characters sang veiled pleas for resistance.

⁴⁸ He made the first doll with closing eyes. Toys revered him as the sleep-giver. In truth, he had secrets to hide even from his mute creations.

⁴⁹ In the aftermath of civilisation, the devout did not have golden cathedrals. Their mosaics were shattered

pavement and broken windows were their stained glass. They congregated in ruins where old pipes caught the wind just right, offering organ music for their simple hymns.

⁵⁰ Of course, the hotel really did have a thirteenth floor. It slithered between walls and around elevators, stalking guests after check-out time.

⁵¹ 'Evil is a base state,' he argued, 'passive and pervasive, while virtue requires effort. Thus, things lacking an agenda can be evil: objects, locations, even days or years. If I tell you this coffee maker is evil, its lack of free will should not stop me from getting a refund.'

⁵² The neglected castle grew, pulling stone after stone from the earth. It would catch a new master or mistress, and be powerful once again.

⁵³ By fear or temptation, madness or deceit, every dream fights to ensnare the dreamer and prolong itself. When we go to sleep, we go to war.

⁵⁴ The creature thrived on ignorance. You could always tell which town it was targeting next. The library would burn down, phones would fail, bridges would collapse. Books left unattended were torn to shreds. Even street signs would go missing. Oddly, the Internet never crashed.

⁵⁵ Whale song and steam whistle are dialects of the same language. Trains feared coastal tracks, where they heard beautiful dirges from below.

⁵⁶ It was easy to spot those who had been banned from dreaming. They stared hatefully at birds, slowly forgetting what it felt like to fly.

⁵⁷ We never bothered telling aliens about our folklore. Yet reports of human ghosts along their shorelines always began after our first visit.

⁵⁸ A watched pot never boils.
A tree won't sing when you can hear.
A star can't die if you believe in it.
Stop believing.
The star is so tired.

⁵⁹ Dejected, the ghost watched the stranger turn and walk away. It was as beautiful as it could be, draped in white with auburn hair, framed by the moon in a field of lavender. Long ago, it lured folk into the woods with a smile. Now they knew when something was too good to be true.

⁶⁰ His daughter's favourite cartoon spoke to the audience, waiting for replies to encourage participation. Eventually he noticed the colourful characters were really obeying her. She didn't like one, and told it to

go away. He saw fear in its eyes as it walked, smiling, off-screen.

[61] Fireworks get their properties from composition:
Red: Strontium
Green: Barium chloride
Blue: Copper chloride
Whistling: Potassium benzoate
Whispering ancient secrets: Gold from shipwrecks in the Blind Sea
Shouting our own secrets: We don't know, please make them stop

[62] His trumpet took extraordinary twists and turns. It was not a musical instrument, but a brass labyrinth in which silence could be timelessly lost. The music was not his breath, but the roaring of a shining Minotaur guarding the valves from within. This, of course, was cheating.

[63] Countless confessions of love were made during the near-apocalypse. Everyone agreed to ignore 'les amours finales', but none were forgotten.

[64] The meteorologist didn't stop, forecasting further and further into the future. Sooner than expected, there was no more weather to report.

[65] Metaphysical ailments called for unique medicine. Hospitals hired professional umbrists to examine,

diagnose, and treat patients' shadows. Fluctuation in shape or length was easily treated, but shade syndrome was dire, with shadows burning and scratching humans when touched. Retroptimologists treated diseases and conditions of the reflection with a variety of medicinal mirrors made of exotic metals. Sanguivore tools allowed the doctors to work on the patient, but not his reflection. Spectral tools did the opposite, but were easily lost. The most difficult new specialty conferred the letters VS, for Vox Secundo. It dealt with illness, silence or malice in the patient's echo. In the worst cases echoes could turn feral, insulting their masters and publicly shouting their secrets. Heterodyne dialysis was required.

[66] 'I can tell there's something between them,' she said. 'I mean, I can only see it by looking between them, like their bodies are some kind of door frame. It's horrible, all hunched over and drooling. I think it's watching us. It's hard to tell, but I'm not getting any closer.'

[67] Zombies that muttered 'brains' never lasted long. Successful ghouls had more effective phrases.

'Everybody knows.'

'You have no secrets.'

'Fraaaud.'

Survivors stayed far away from their barricaded doors, trying to avoid the harsh words. They never heard their defences break.

CHAPTER 10

Weird

[1] There are 21 million cubic feet of molten rock and metal directly below every square foot of Earth. There is literally nothing hiding you from every star, galaxy and sunless planet in the night sky. Cosmically speaking, your back is against the wall.

[2] Galaxies were mere tide pools. The empty space between them was a killing field of dark-matter predators and electromagnetic anglerfish.

[3] She crept through the clown temple, clutching her seltzer gun. Rubber chickens and balloon animals had been freshly sacrificed on the altar.

[4] He made dismantling cults and strangling abominations seem effortless, but she'd never seen anyone have to work so hard just to look happy.

⁵ She cringed at the cultist's smile. It had the same crawling, backward wrongness she felt whenever she saw a spider eat a mouse or a bird.

⁶ His vigil for the return of his master grew tedious. Eventually he just did Internet searches for 'intractable laughter' and 'drooling pitch'.

⁷ 'With time,' she whispered, 'all languages return to the root tongue used by the elder things of the universe. It is a language of worship.'

⁸ He found the sanctum of the astronomy cult with its ceiling of 10,000 lenses. Together they burned sacrifices in the light of Polaris.

⁹ He hesitated to approach. She was armed with a fistful of poems, each one honed to a razor's edge and lovingly crafted for him alone. There were still parts of his heart left unscarred, and she knew exactly how to reach them. He had to trust her, and nothing was more frightening.

¹⁰ Briefly, driving on a dark road, he saw a creature that didn't belong in his world. The fear lingered. Reality was larger than he'd thought.

¹¹ The first movies did have audio tracks, but the weighty eldritch words in early scripts overwhelmed the fragile medium, rendering it silent.

¹² Space itself took human shape and came down to walk among us. That wasn't nearly so glorious and frightening as what then filled the sky.

¹³ 'Enjoy your childhood,' older generations said. 'An elder will eventually transfer his mind into your body. So enjoy yourself. Quickly.'

¹⁴ The townsfolk would not swim in that lake, and no boat dared to cross it. It was one of the few places where the ocean that surged within the planet reached out to the surface on dry land. By night, the village shook with the songs of jet-black whales that came to see the moon.

¹⁵ 'Excuse me, sir,' the gentleman said. 'Last year the Asylum returned you to full mental health. Your bill remains unpaid. I'm the repo man.'

¹⁶ The book fascinated her. That was the danger. She slowly starved, unable to look away. She grew new pairs of eyes to absorb the text faster.

¹⁷ Rumours said that she was an ocean creature dwelling on land. She chilled her drink with ice-cold pearls, paid shopkeepers with salty gold coins, glared at lighthouses, and wore dresses of a very convincing sea-foam green. He nervously accepted her invitation to walk on the beach.

[18] Visiting servants of alien suns were the first to suggest humans wish upon the stars. The practice has yielded their masters valuable intel.

[19] Logic said the unearthly things he saw by the road at night were just tricks of shadows and negative space. Yet logic couldn't protect him.

[20] 'I have purpose for you beyond the physical,' she said, opening the book. 'You're like wire before electricity, used only for its strength.'

[21] The massive creature entered Earth's orbit, looking down on us with unknowable emotions. Its skin glowed to mimic the stars behind it. However, when day came, the beast apparently didn't know our sky would be blue. We didn't reveal that we could see it, lest we hurt its feelings.

[22] 'Something old rests here, stirring in the earth,' she whispered. 'To aliens we are as lion tamers, our courage and recklessness shocking.'

[23] He had been the one to send her into the Singularity to root out the cybercult. Now he just wanted her to be happy with being human again.

[24] At first the creatures in the looking glass were an annoyance, but their numbers grew until mirrors showed nothing but their teeth and eyes.

²⁵ A small cadre learned to project their minds into others. The rest of us fled to the wild places, lest we be taken and worn like clothing.

²⁶ With mosquitoes extinct, something else stepped into the vacant niche. Blood is a common resource, and this other thing would see it tapped.

²⁷ Up close, it was clear that the snake's body was actually a tentacle, devoid of bones but lined with hooks and suction discs. It instinctively wriggled away toward the sea. She could see thousands more along the beach, as though they were assembling into something grander.

²⁸ The forest reclaimed its ancient lands from the city by force. As we fled, it took no spoils of war, but kept children to raise as its own.

²⁹ Smiling, he stood to leave, but couldn't let go of her hand. She didn't want him to go. Her tentacle tattoos had coiled around his wrist.

³⁰ Tiny scratches on the inner crystals of the geode were translated as desperate pleas for exoneration and apologies to a subterranean king.

³¹ For years you have censored your mind. You avoid remembering secrets needlessly, lest they be overheard.

You skip over cartoons and cheesy songs to keep your inner child presentably mature.

I get it. Old habits die hard. But they haven't reached Earth yet. Relax while you can.

[32] His reflection, unhappy with his mundane life, found one of its own. It began showing up with scars he didn't have, and an ever-wilder smile.

[33] He'd given blood, but they told him to stay seated. They connected him to books, lanterns, the soil outside. Yes, he had much left to give.

[34] He rode out to face the golf cult in the cart he'd commandeered from their shrine, dragging a club bag and leading their liberated caddies.

[35] Bonfires gave us our first clue that something was wrong. The smoke stopped smelling like sweet, charred wood, and reeked instead of the sea. We looked closer, and found that plants worldwide were changing their chemistry to resemble ocean flora. They were preparing for something.

[36] We all felt a knocking from outside our reality. Scientists debated whether to open a door, pointing out that at least our guest was polite.

[37] Most vacationers weren't ready for 'luxury cruises'

beyond Earth. They came back quieter, gently offering tribute to a king we couldn't see.

[38] We finally explored the ocean floor, and with knowledge came fear. Our lighthouses were lit once more, now to warn people away from the sea.

[39] The game of tag was invented long ago to train children how to avoid nameless, body-swapping ghosts. Any we met were called simply 'it'.

[40] He arrived at his destination, but the voice of the GPS app kept giving orders. She led him to ancient books, to old prayers. He sang the songs she couldn't.

[41] Laughter is the best medicine.
Hunger is the best spice.
Fire is the best friend.
The sky is the best hiding spot.
We haven't seen them yet.

[42] As humans lived for millennia, even the instincts we thought were hardwired got overwritten. Our fear of the dark became a fear of the night sky and the eyes hiding among the stars. Loneliness was replaced by a creeping panic, felt whenever we were separate from the hive mind.

[43] As our technology advanced, existential dread became

a hot commodity. People paid for the secrets of physicists and philosophers that could still invoke the innate human fear of extinction. Jumpy colonists returning from deep space promised we wouldn't need that service for long.

[44] Vitamin F: Vital to promoting cross-sensory perception. Deficiency causes an inability to see temperature or sense colours through the skin.

Vitamin G: Plentiful in most diets, this protein keeps Earth's life invisible to stellar behemoths. Deficiency can cause planetary doom.

Vitamin H: Every molecule of it is quantum-entangled to the original on a distant world. Deficiency causes the patient to seek that place.

Vitamin I: Bonds to bad-luck free radicals that would otherwise cause grave misfortune. Deficiency often manifests as unexpected lightning.

Vitamin J: This protein is active but has no clear purpose. Yet, when the portals open, it will show us which to enter. Deficiency fatal.

Vitamin K: Found in leafy greens, it assists in blood clotting and healthy bone construction. Deficiency causes bleeding and calcification.

Vitamin L: Exists across all possible realities. If one of your parallel selves becomes weak, this protein saps the strength of that runt.

Vitamin M: This acid is protective against the intense radiation near the galactic core. Alien civilisations depleted Earth's entire supply.

Vitamins N & O: Gold and red pigments that allowed a full range of colour in human eyes. Source plants were rare, and nobles ate them into extinction for the prestige of scarlet eyes.

[45] The thunderstorm lived on in the memories of those who had lived through it. For years they bore it, baulking at the sun, cherishing every gust of wind, and growling after camera flashes. When the storm would no longer be fractured, they gathered once more. The sky grew dark.

[46] A hundred broken gingerbread men lay on the rock-candy altar of the sugar cult. He brandished his insulin, hearing their toothless chants.

[47] The first one to wash ashore was a curiosity: a blue-black seashell, big as a house and matching no known creature, its spirals made to guard a thousand tentacles. The next year, the beaches grew dark. We looked closer, and found that more tiny shells outnumbered grains of sand.

[48] This has been a test of the Reality Alert System. If this had been a real emergency you would be advised to:
- Reset your compasses to 'zero'.
- Lock all books and maps in an airtight container.
- Make sure everyone in your household is blindfolded.
- Wait for The Singing to pass.

⁴⁹ She said she would pull down the moon to prove her love for him. Now the sky was on fire, the satellite crashing because he had doubted her.

⁵⁰ The building had pull-alarms unlike any he'd seen, striped black and green. He asked when he should use them. He was told, 'You'll know.'

⁵¹ Society was delighted to find that, unlike most others, he did not worship himself. Those hoping to become his new deity began sending gifts.

⁵² Shredded Jolly Rogers underfoot, he sang aloud in the lair of the money cult. Its acolytes hated music because wealth could not improve it.

⁵³ Miners didn't go to deep space for rare elements. Their lonely ships returned to Earth brimming with the creeping fear of the unknown, gathered meticulously in the parts of space where the sun's light faded to black. That cargo was in short supply on our tamed, automated planet.

⁵⁴ **The Millennial Muses**
After the nightmare of postmodernism had passed, recovering artists needed new subjects untethered to things as fickle as history or reality. Thus, nine new muses were invented to embody modern endeavour:

- Oiale, the muse of mechanics, is depicted as having hand-like simian feet and gearwork patterns painted in grease all over her muscled arms.
- Artists usually depict Shoneme, muse of con-artistry, as having a silver tongue. Savvy sculptors know it should really be made of tin.
- Tannhause, muse of science fiction, is depicted as a smiling, extraterrestrial angel, reaching for the sky as her feet trample civilisation.
- Graphene is the only valid statuary medium to depict Palygone, the two-dimensional muse of computer programming, shown covered in pythons.
- Troba, muse of YouTube, is depicted with a voxel sword in one hand and a smartphone in the other, followed by her cats Like and Subscribe.
- Murmure, muse of nuclear physics, is depicted as scarred but beautiful, holding a basket of mushrooms and wearing a flowing gown of lead.
- Statues of Naseti, muse of space travel, should be made of meteoric iron and depict the helmeted figure upside down, arms open to humanity.
- Loje, muse of truth, is meant to be unseen. Overeager artists over the ages sculpted her, ignoring the implied truth that muses aren't real.
- Insomnia, the cruel and wild muse, is never depicted as calm or serene. Her mad smile makes her plainly identifiable even in pitch darkness.

CHAPTER 11

Other

Song Lyrics

The Time Traveller's Lullaby

It's time to rest and stop running for a while.
(Mummy/Daddy) let the sky go dark so the stars could
    appear.
Out of all of history, and any given day,
There is no sweeter time or place for us to be than here.

Because...

This is the moment (Mummy/Daddy) picked just for
    you.
The moon is bright, the wind is soft, and it's time for
    counting sheep.
We can just lie back and let the night go by.

We're headed for tomorrow, and we'll get there in our
    sleep.

The future is full of amazing things to see,
Of planets full of mystery, and our robotic friends,
But they can wait until you've gotten forty winks,
So let the night go slowly, as the universe intends.

Because...

This is the moment (Mummy/Daddy) picked just for
    you.
What a comfy, stable timeline that you and I have
    found.
We can just lie back and let the night go by.
We're headed for tomorrow, and we'll take the long way
    round.

You can dream of our days spent in the past,
The scenery by Zeppelin, or the mammoths in the snow.
Don't you fret about making Caesar mad.
It wasn't really our fault, and he passed on long ago.

That's why...

This is the moment (Mummy/Daddy) picked just for you.
An instant of tranquillity, in a brief historic hush.
We can just lie back and let the night go by.
We're headed for tomorrow, but there's no need to rush.

The Twelve Lost Days of Christmas

Version 1 (2020)

On the twelfth day of Christmas the pine trees gave to me: twelve sea-glass arrows, ancient weapons used by sailors to fight back against foul weather, far too small to actually slay a storm but enough to make it think twice about letting its lightning strike too close to my ship

Eleven morning nails, which will not budge or break unless the sun is shining, long used by rural gravediggers to seal the caskets of the undead by night to buy time until more experienced vampire hunters can be called, or as leverage to strike bargains with the monsters inside

Ten soul-wax candles, each barely larger than a toothpick, whose flames and smoke will be drawn to the nearest living person other than the one who lights them; of little use on Earth but invaluable in deep space, where finding another beating heart in the void can be impossible

Nine cups of dew, taken from places in the forest humans have not seen yet, so the magical parts of the forest will not flee at my approach, and so I can join woodland fairies in their mushroom circles but not be compelled to keep dancing until I die from exhaustion

Eight azure keys, tattooed on my arm, each one able to open the way for me through a mental block, like a persistent phobia, a concept I just cannot seem to understand, or the anxious refusal to confess my love, with the promise that I will need all of them in the next year

Seven cobblestones, grey and unassuming, to be placed along the path to my front door to guarantee visitors on days when the sun is shining and the wind is cool, though I was warned that the results could be quite unexpected if I place them outside a habitat on the moon or Mars

Six dark equations, to be completed in times of cataclysm, that will adjust our understanding of physical laws to account for miracles in the past, revealing secrets of higher dimensions for me to ponder to ward off memetic attacks of the enemy and the despair they will bring

FIVE GOLD RINGS

Four figurines, tiny animals carved from salt, to be crushed or dissolved into my dinner before bed, that I might dream through the creatures' eyes by night, though I do not recognise their species, and fear to see the ocean depths or far-off worlds they might inhabit

Three passwords, approved by the Forest King, to be repeated to his army depending on the path I take during his invasion: to be spared by the forces of the forest, to enlist as a noble overseer of their advancement, or to remain loyal to humanity and decide my fate in single combat

Two Merlin rooks, bright and talkative little fellows, who experience time in reverse, and will repeat things they remember hearing in the future, so I can be forearmed with words and phrases that I will say either with great frequency or great desperation

And a bag of feather-light seeds, specially grown by the plants of the wood after word spread that humanity might leave this world, and that heavy things are frowned upon during space travel, so I can take the forest with me, and never be without the quiet pine trees.

Version 2 (2018)

On the twelfth day of Christmas, the pine trees gave to me: twelve golden matches, each capable of brightening words rather than shadows, to be used in moments when the need for eloquence is too great to be trusted to the feeble wits of mortal minds

Eleven figures chanting, their grey hooded robes difficult to spot as they dwell on the far edge of my perception, their synchronised whispers almost lost in the noise of the modern world as they relay information about me to something that lives in a colder, smaller universe

Ten willow tears, delicacies of the Forest King himself, so full of the season of autumn they make my breath condense in the air and my fingers leave golden stains on the foliage, so the denizens of the woods will know me as a friend

Nine bits and bobs, trinkets recovered from the wreckage of my own time machine, still somewhat recognisable despite the char, so that I can get some clues about my future, and know that the machine won't crash until I've found each of them on my own

Eight granite bowls, one of which will turn ordinary river water into an elixir to cure ageing, so that I and seven others can play a single round of Immortality Roulette and see who will have to live long enough to see the forests wither and die

Seven copper chains, each with one end affixed in the past and the other in the future; an old-fashioned and reckless form of time travel, to be held tightly to slow the passage of halcyon days, or traversed to reach future moments that are too good to wait for

Six hidden words, once reserved for poets whose skill left no challenge in ordinary vocabulary, to succinctly convey things that otherwise evade easy description, like the relief of knowing you've been snowed in, or fear at the realisation of what you could accomplish

FIVE GOLD RINGS

Four violet birds, able to see the rising and ebbing tide of fate, that will sing their fearful song together as moments of destiny approach just as roosters crow before the dawn, so I will be forewarned when the Forest War has at last begun

Three jade teeth, found washed up on the shore of a spring-fed lake, hinting at the stone monsters that lurk below its waves, or perhaps deep underground in the heart of the spring, so I can warn the rest of humanity of their presence, if I so choose

Two vellum shoes, covered in gentle adjectives, made for traversing stories rather than roads; to be worn in the inhospitable land of dreams, so that even when the narrative becomes dark and frightful, I can find my way to a happy ending

And the words to a silent song, one I can sing to myself in the brightest or bleakest places to see myself back in the forest, to hear its sounds and feel its shadows, and never forget that my place, my true home, is among the quiet pine trees.

Version 3 (2017)

On the twelfth day of Christmas the pine trees gave to me: twelve hidden hours, a secret third half to each day as the sun rings the horizon, when we can finally admit what's in our hearts, because not a word of it will be remembered

Eleven daytime stars, dark points in a bright sky, a constellation pointing me to the lands I imagined were there as a child, making it impossible to ignore them again

Ten ancient poisons, each dose just barely strong enough to kill a moment's worth of doubt, brewed from indigo flowers that were harvested to extinction during an age that was starved of heroes

Nine words of warning, whispered within the songs of crickets and scrawled in my own handwriting between the stars: 'The sea will be your only refuge from them'

Eight caves of silver, carved by miners who left behind the precious metal either because something all the more seductive was calling to them from below, or because they were only seeking to hide from something calling to them from above

Seven amber statues, depicting those who will be my enemies in the years to come, so that by contemplating their sad smiles I can be ready for them, forgive them before we even meet, and perhaps understand why one of them is me

Six guardian snowmen, absolutely still and forever unblinking, their eyes locked on the sky, ready to cry out at the sight of an approaching figure from the void, so that I can finally rest from my vigil

FIVE GOLD RINGS

Four wooden coins, the currency of the seasons, just enough to pay for a single summer to turn to autumn, to wrap the world in darkling sweetness as the storms and frost drown out the sun

Three bone pins, carved from the skeletons of long-extinct creatures, which will ward against misfortune, having already been tempered with all the bad luck they can endure

Two loyal dogs, skyhounds who will never stop seeking out crashed starships and time travellers, eager as they are to take me away from this planet and show me the silent wonders of their playground universe

And a wooden crown beset with lake stones, a priceless heirloom of the Forest King himself, given as a test of my humility, to see if I will cast it aside and accept my place among the quiet pine trees.

Version 4 (2016)

On the twelfth day of Christmas the pine trees gave to me: twelve ancient dances, lost because our coddled souls can't follow their native rhythms

Eleven silver deserts, reflecting and magnifying the minds of wanderers so the stars can see the unfamiliar emotions that come from being lost

Ten blue-green stones that appear over and over again, following me and disrupting my life because it's been too long since I visited the sea

Nine black-market meals, free of the custom pharmaceuticals and radioactive tracers that alert the establishment whenever we've been reading

Eight night-sky horses, wormhole hearts pumping plasma from an alien sun, dark-matter hooves breaking flecks of gravity from the cobblestones

Seven unseen colours, the infrared palette of moonless nights and endless caves, invitation to an inner world that cowards leave behind

Six loyal lakes, awaiting orders to swallow my old

life like Usher ruins, wash me of civilisation's electric dust, and build my castle of fog

FIVE GOLD RINGS

Four minutes sealed in acrylic, to be released in defiance of time itself when a perfect moment, one worth fighting to keep, threatens to end

Three new names, the true names by which I am called in dreams, so my heart can defend itself from the lonely horrors of that unwaking world

Two comet hearts, the spark of cosmic wildness still burning within, ready to escort myself and a guest in a hasty escape from the planet

And a chance to join their fabled ranks, to glimpse the mirror in Plato's cave, and deny the truth no more loudly than the quiet pine trees.

Micro-Mysteries

1. A locked house. A tall staircase. A dead butler at the bottom. The moon is full. A lamp is missing from a table near the body. Music is playing upstairs. Payday was three days ago. Only four people were home. Whodunit?
A. Alchemist chef
B. Time-travelling maid
C. Zombie valet
D. Ghost gardener

2. A rare coin, the gold double-leopard, vanished from the museum overnight. Four people had keys.

A second coin was scheduled to join the display the next day. The Taurid meteors were ending. The basement pipes had been replaced. The boiler was on. Who took it?

A. Vampire curator

B. Telepath janitor

C. Sentient brown-bear guard

D. Maintenance ghost

3. The lighthouse keeper was stabbed in his own lantern room. His wife found him at midnight. They were avid divers who recovered sunken treasures, which were taken. The door was unlocked. It was summer. Whodunit?

A. Gnome neighbour

B. Zombie milkman

C. Salty old robot sailor

D. Vampirates

4. The last human on Earth was fatally stabbed in his home in the woods. Robot police found his doors locked. The doorknobs were round. The old man's money had been taken; it was not enough to buy passage to off-planet human colonies. Two cups of coffee had been set out. Whodunit?

A. Confused snowman

B. Out-of-work scarecrow

C. Desperate vampire

D. Time-travelling past self

Solutions:

1. With regular pay and a light-hearted atmosphere, there appears to be little motive for a murder. However, any member of the staff would want to conceal their involvement in an accidental death. This is especially true if that death took place during a non-work-related activity.

As with most workers, payday for this crew was Friday. That means the butler died on Monday. Since the family of the house wasn't home, the music upstairs was for the benefit of the staff. The moon was full, so the mood was romantic, or at least whimsical. It is entirely plausible that the butler fell down the stairs while dancing. But with whom?

The valet is off the hook. Zombies haven't danced since 1982, and 'Thriller' isn't very romantic.

Gainful employment is a rare thing for ghosts. The gardener wouldn't risk such a nice job by slacking off on a Monday.

That leaves the chef and the maid. The lamp is the key to the mystery. It was likely smashed in the butler's fall. It is missing because the guilty party cleaned up the mess. The chef's domain is the kitchen, and cleaning up a broken lamp there would be natural. However, while many are connected to cellars, few kitchens have staircases leading to the upper floors. Additionally, most kitchens use overhead lighting rather than lamps. Thus the death was not in the kitchen.

The maid would have felt the need to clean up the mess made by the butler's death. With her time-travel powers, she and the butler could also afford to spend a few minutes dancing together, even on a Monday. You can travel into the past to finish your duties at work, but you can't undo a death you caused without creating a paradox. Therefore the maid is the most likely suspect. She may not be a murderer, but she probably did tamper with evidence.

But, as with all mysteries, in the end, the butler did it.

2. The curator is immediately off the hook. The double-leopard, also known as the Edward III double florin, featured a royal cross on the reverse side. As a vampire, the curator could not have handled the coin safely.

The janitor is not a likely culprit either. Even though he's just a janitor, he is also a telepath, so he would have known the new coin would be added to the display soon. He could have doubled his loot if he'd just waited another night.

The maintenance ghost would have been working all night in the basement, away from the exhibits. As a ghost, he can only work at night, and was clearly diligent, as his task was completed by dawn. The boiler was on, so he didn't even have anywhere to stash the coin while he worked, since the furnace could damage it.

The Taurid meteor shower is an annual event, and if it was just wrapping up, then the caper happened in mid-autumn. This means, as a bear, the guard would have been preparing for hibernation. He would have used up all his resources to prepare, and would still need money for recovery in the spring.

The bear took the coin. With a looming hibernation deadline, he couldn't wait for any new coins to be added. He planned to sell the coin in the spring, when the heat was off.

3. The vampirates are the obvious suspects, but the circumstances make that unlikely. Vampires must be invited into buildings, meaning they are the only suspects for whom the door was effectively locked. Their seagoing lifestyle also means they would have to drop anchor and row ashore to reach the lighthouse, which the victim would definitely have seen.

While the milkman's proximity seems unusual, it actually makes perfect sense. With his limited mobility, the zombie milkman would want to avoid making his routes during the heat of the day in summer. He would naturally deliver milk at night to keep it fresh. He is also unlikely to make the long, dangerous climb to the lantern room, and could not have done so and made his getaway in the short hours between dusk and midnight.

Similarly, the gnomish neighbour is unlikely to make the climb to the lantern room when he could much more easily sneak in to steal the goods on the lower floors. Further, in all likelihood, such a diminutive creature would be unable to deliver a fatal stabbing to a grown man. If he was intent on killing the lighthouse keeper, he would be more likely to trip his victim down the stairs.

The most likely suspect is therefore the salty old robot sailor. As a mighty and sleepless robot, he would have the physical strength to kill the lighthouse keeper and make a quick getaway. He had means and opportunity. Like any old sailor, the robot would have known plenty of other sailors lost to the sea near his port of call. Some of these would have been fellow robots. That provides motive, since the lighthouse keeper and his wife were taking valuables from shipwrecks, presumably including precious metals used to build sailing robots. The robot killed the lighthouse keeper not just for his gold, but to give his fellow automaton sailors a proper burial.

4. Right away we can eliminate the poor, innocent snowman as a suspect. His snowy hands are too smooth to use a round doorknob, much less activate the lock. The victim would also not offer a snowman coffee, even iced coffee, since it would still be warmer than snow and therefore destructive to the snowman's body.

The scarecrow is also an unlikely candidate. While it would be more likely to accept a cup of coffee, a scarecrow has no brains, and would therefore lack the wit to escape the locked house after the murder.

Additionally, both the snowman and scarecrow lack motive. Human emotions give purpose to snowmen, and human needs give purpose to scarecrows, so killing the last human on the planet would make them disposable in the eyes of their pragmatic robot overlords.

The vampire initially seems like a good suspect, since the lack of humans on the planet would certainly provide a motive to attack the victim. A vampire, able to change into smaller creatures like a bat, would also have no problem escaping the home after the murder, through the chimney.

However, the method of the murder eliminates the motive, since vampires do not feed by stabbing their victims. The money would not provide enough motivation for the vampire, either. This human lived in the forest, where wooden implements that could kill a vampire would be easy to find or make, and he didn't even have enough money to buy passage to other human colonies. It would make more sense for the vampire to attack and steal from robots, which could have more money and would live in less dangerous surroundings.

The culprit was the victim's own time-travelling younger self. The victim would certainly recognise himself and offer hospitality, like a cup of coffee. Robbing his older self would allow the perpetrator to easily claim his own money, return to the past, and repeat the process until he could afford to buy a ticket to another planet. And obviously, leaving the scene of the crime via time travel would allow the doors to stay locked.

Supporters' Stories

Many people helped make this collection possible. As the book was being developed, some amazing people offered so much support that they got the opportunity to request their own custom stories on whatever topics they liked. To them I say, thank you.

Dan Keen

Fairies don't always fly. Sometimes they walk, searching the ground for marvellous things. They know where to find the best magic pebbles and tastiest flowers. Sharp-eyed hikers can spot the fairies' little trails along the forest floor, crisscrossing our own, formed by tiny feet.

Kendra Baxter

As a runt, the dog never fit in with its rough and tumble siblings. It preferred the gentle company of birds. Nuthatches taught the dog to climb upside down. Owls shared the secrets of darkling silence. The crows were the kindest, spying on humans to learn the words 'good dog'.

Thomas and Brooke Darling

A patch of wild time crossed the country road. The family marvelled as the sky filled with space stations, starships and skyscrapers too wondrous to be made from known materials. They stopped and turned the camper around. They were on vacation, and this future would ruin their stargazing.

A Note on the Author

T. R. Darling is an award-winning journalist from Michigan, USA. He started his career in radio before becoming a television news producer. He began writing microfiction on social media as a way to explore his love for weird, creative stories while working long and unpredictable hours, and has since embraced the ultra-short format as a legitimate literary medium. The themes in *Quiet Pine Trees* are inspired by time spent in the deep forests of northern Michigan during his youth. Darling says all of his microfiction stories exist within a single narrative canon.

Index

Index

Index

Index

Unbound is the world's first crowdfunding publisher, established in 2011.

We believe that wonderful things can happen when you clear a path for people who share a passion. That's why we've built a platform that brings together readers and authors to crowdfund books they believe in – and give fresh ideas that don't fit the traditional mould the chance they deserve.

This book is in your hands because readers made it possible. Everyone who pledged their support is listed below. Join them by visiting unbound.com and supporting a book today.

Alex Accornero
Debby Accuardi
Chad Adams
Peyton Adams
Jonathon Adamy
Katharine Adcroft
Kat Ahl
Stacey Ahrens
@akaTheReader
Jacob Albano
Rob Alexander
Teresa Altarriba

Karjan Amahel
Anna C.M Andersson
Johanna Andersson
Rokkor Andrews
Sallie Ann
Elisa Antila
Theese Aregon
Stacie Arellano metahari
Sandra Aristo
Evan Armour
Isabel Arreaza
Stuart Ashen

S Aziz
Dom B
Karen B
Monica B
Faustina B.
Teddy B.
Annika Baier
David Baillie
Katy Balagopal
Jason Ballinger
Sarah Barber
Esteban Barboza
Quincy Barclais
Jenna Barrett
Erik Barrows
LJ Barrows
Matt Bartels
Marie Barton
Daniel Bates
Kendra Baxter
Eugenia Belinskaya
Alan Belsky
Jennifer Bendell
Marie-Christine Bernier
Samantha Bigelow
Michael Bikovitsky
Katrina Bilbrey
Andrew Bishop
Rob Blackburn
Logan Blackisle
Florentin Blanc
Autumn Blogg
Roger Blunden
Ken Board
Kristin Bodreau
David Bofinger
Brent Bolin

J Botari
Christian Brehm
Colette Breshears
Catherine Breslin
Lexie Briggs
Chris Brinkley
Zoë Brouns
Ash Brown
A Browne
Joseph Budway
Erica Burdick
Emily Burgardt
Brandi Burnett
Peter Burns
Florian Büther
Amanda Butler
Joey Butler
Rowan Butler
Eric Cabello
Kaiden Cadek
Chase Campbell
Sam Carlier
Carter
Alice Cartes
Mary Catelli
Rebecca Chacon
John Luke Chapman
Poe Charlotte
Samantha Chau
Celia Cheung
Anthony Chivetta
Lu Chou
Kirsten Christiansen
Garth Clardy
Richard Clarkson
Ashley Claycomb
Alex Clayden

Bo Cline
Emzzy Cole
Oliver Cole
Timo Conrady
Harry Cooke
Will Cooper
Sarah Cornell
Gabriel Cornyn
Paige Cotton
Conrad Cotton-Barratt
Janelle Cottrell
Robert Cox
Hope Crandall
K Cummings
David Curley
Alicia Curtis
Louise Dalton
Rachel Daly
Maya Dancey
Brooke Darling
Brooke & Thomas Darling
Grandma & Grandpa
 Darling
James Darling
Thomas Darling Sr
Jess Davey
Al Davidson
Emma Davies
Joachim Davis
Joseph Dayes
Lynelle Dea
Stacey Dearing
Kate DeForest
Menno Deij
Mia del Barrio
Frog Delacroix
Zeb Delk

Alexandra DeLonay
Michael Demetriou
Adrian Di Rago
Lisa Dickson
Audrey DiFelice
Shane Digiovanna
Ashley Dillon
Christine Diorio
Rain Doggerel
Ben Doran
Linda Doughty
Sarah Doukakos
Ryan Doyle
Elizabeth Dran
S. R. Dreamholde
L. C. Duesterhoeft
Jacob Edwards
Jed Edwards
Andy Ellis
Ryan Ellison
Makayla Emery
Diana Engelhardt
Mati England
Mikkel Kamstrup
 Erlandsen
Michael Esau
Sydney Estes
v f
Jennie Faries
Sharareh Farivar
Robert Farley
Meridith Felice
Marisa Fernandez
Richard Ferrante
Megs Ferrone
Mar Fidelman
Alexander Field

Evan Fields
Spencer Fleury
Thomas Flott
Emily Fogarty
Valentin Foley
E. Forney
Britt Heidi Fossum
Sandy Fougerousse
Dany Fox
Peggy Frank
Fay Franklin
Marcus Frowerk
Alberto Fuentes Agustí
Mark Funk
Stephane Gallant
Vivienne Gao
Elizabeth Gardner
Toni Gee
Anne Geeske
Catherine Geiger
Samantha Gignac
Michael Gipson
Thomas Gleason
Gordon Glenn
Giles Goodland
Emma Goodwin
Keegan Gordon
Amy Gore
Laurie Gravell
Alex Greene
Kaitlyn Grier
Michael Grunert
Beth Guest
Jennifer H
Alex Hacker
Alastair 'Oh Hey a Funny
  Pseudonym' Haig

Victoria Haimov
Natalina Halas
Aaron Hans
Michael Hanscom
Reece Harbour
John Harkin
Isabel Harman
Nathaniel Harrison
Paul G Harrop
Irish Harvey
Jan Havlík
Morgan Hay
Lyra Healy
Sean Healy
Niall Hedderley
Cat Heeley
Anssi Matti Helin
Stephanie Henrichs Welch
Joshua Hepworth
Kadijah Herbert
Lou Herlitz
Rob Herman
Pascal Hertleif
Adrian Hickford
Jorden Hiscock
Margaret Hogg
Jenna Holschen
Jenni Hopper
Kit Houseman
Madeline Huber
Maddison Hunt
Wes Hunt
Justice Hunter
Leisha Hussien
Sheryl Hutcherson
Hamish Hutchings
is8ac

Joseph itendswithz
Maggie Jack
Samantha Jackson
Robin Jacobs
Augusto Jacquier
Ceri James
Lee Jaschok
Jenni
JK
Stephanie Johnson
Kellen Johnston
Ieuan Jones
Julia
Daniel Kaliba
D Kan
Ashe Karin
Kassidy
Alex Katakis
Dan Keen
Nicolas Khouri
Dan Kieran
Angela Kilian
Rook Killjoy
John Kilpatrick
Brindi Kisamore
Kittenpox
Katriena Knights
Michaela Knowles
John Koutrouba
Jan Krupička
Rebecca Kuipers
Tara Kustermann
Eevi Laakso
Aaron LaBrie
Dan LaGesse
Ellis Lalonde
Cynthia Lapham

Lawrence Lavigne
Laura Law
Christine Lawton
Yannick Le Berre
Robin Lee
Eric Leimer
Elisabeth Lempa
Elly Lepp
David Levy
Kris Lewis
Gabriel Liang
Myz Lilith
Grant Lilly
Jenny Liu
Isabella Lopez-Powers
Max Lord
Sam Lovelace
Mark Luffel
John Lund
Felice Cat-Tuong Luu
Anna Lyaruu
Tessa Lyne
David Lyon
Cooper Lyons
Heather Lyons
Mackinaw Mackinaw
Angus Macleod
Bridget MacLeod
Erin MacLeod
Petra Majlath
Jane Malcolm
Gabrielle Mansfield
Gray Martin
Briana May
Kristin May
Kate McAlpine
Colleen McCaffrey

Lucy McCahon
Willard McClellan
Joe McCollom
Jon McCorkell
Jonathan McDermott
David McElligott
Ariel McFalls
Marie McGinley
Edward McKee
William McLelland
Darcy McLeod
Ian McMahan
Andrea McNeil
Francis McNeill
Moniquill Medicine Crow
Caleb Melchior
Emily Mellors
Korey Mendes
Michela Menghini
Tim Meo
Neima Meymandi
Philip Middleton
Ann Mielke
Allister Mills
Joshua Minor
John Mitchinson
Deena Mobbs
Caitlyn Modaff
David Monteith
John E Monteith
Alexandra Montoya
Peter Moore
William Moore
Nicholas Morgan
Kristen Morici
Kristina Morse
Kat Mort

Geoffrey Moses
Douglas Mosher
Lyle Moulson
Kirby Moyers
Micah Mueller
Mark Mullinger
Tamara Munzner
Elizabeth Murgittroyd
Tessa Murphy
Shelby Murrane
Dana Murray
Justin Myers
Stu Nathan
Joshua Natzke
Carlo Navato
Lynne Nelson
Annabella Newton
Jeremy Nickurak
Brian Nixon
Tom Norris
James Norton
Rebecca Nortz
Norwood
Sarah Nottingham
Brian Nowosatka
Lexi Nylander
Magda O
Az O'Grady
Erin O'Kelly
Shannon O'Leary
Alannah Oldfield
Forrest Oliphant
◇Vikki ◇Ong
Sarah Oppelt
Amy Ortega
Vita Osborne
Mona Fosheim Øwre

Alex Pacynko
Rielle Pagan
Sean E. Palmer
María Ana Paolo
Alyssa Pappas
Jim Parkin
Mark Parsons
Russell Pashkutz
Darian Pedford
Sara Penedo Castro
Karen Peper
Michael David Pereira
Theodaria Perth
Thomas Peters
Magnus Petersson
Andrew Pickering
Scott Piper
Alex Poli
Justin Pollard
Katherine Popple
Maia Posten
Martin Pot
Ryan Power
Janet Pretty
Elizabeth Psyck
Thomas Psyck
Linda Puckette
Nina Quill
Danielle Quinn
Juliana Quiroz
Celeste Qvotrup
Colette Reap
Robert Rees
Adrian Reiter
Cat Reynolds
Amy Richards
Courtney E. Richards

Fiona Riddell Pearce
Carl Rigney
Graeme Ringland
Allison Ringler
Leonard Roberge
Laura Roberts
Anne-Sophie Roos
Charlie Rose
Brian Rosenberger
Chris Rowland
Roxanne
rrix
Sheri Rucinski
Lauren Ruffner
Benjamin Russell
Cort Rutherford
Dr S.Lay
Anders Sandberg
Russell Saur
Savnarae
William Scheid
Jenni Schimmels
Brendan Schlagel
Ilka Schmanteck
Megan Schmidt
Maximillian Schwanekamp
Michal Scienski
Phoebe Seiders
Shai Shaffer
Laurence Shapiro
Reese Share
Caroline Shaw
R.C. Shaw
Shawna
Isobel Sheene
Steve Shelton
Den Shewman

Mark Shields
John Shirlaw
David Sidhu
Elísabet Rakel
    Sigurðardóttir
Magnús Sigurðsson
Anna Simmons
Barbara Simmons
Charlotte Sivanathan
Skerr
Stephen Skolnick
Elizabeth Slomba
Brian Smith
Maire Smith
Natalie Smith
Scott Neal Smith
Devon Sobrado
Ryan H Sorensen
Waffle Sorter
Kaj Sotala
Jonathan South
Etta Spangler
Alyssa Spaulding
Stephen Spey
Erin Spratley
AJ Springer
Gray Stanback
Michael Starr
Michael Stevens
Claire Stevenson
Izzy Stevenson
Dorothy Stickney
Kelsey Tull Stilson
Kristi Straley
Adam Strickland
Emily Stuart
Guilherme Stutz Töws

Theresa Sullivan
Jonathan Summerton
Catherine Sutherland
Balázs Szabó
Charlie T
Jim Tarrant
techxplorer
Jillian Tees
Stuart Teisseire
Paul Ducky Tenk
Dylan Theresa
Ashley Thomas
Laura Thompson
Nicholas Thompson
Alma Tiwe
Eamonn Tobin
†Chaplain Tom
Carson Tompkins
Alex Tozzo
Kael Tuggle
Emily Turek
Wil Turner
Ray Vallese
Gert Van Gool
Tony Vanderheyden
Kassandra Velez
vexingcosmos
Agram Vielt and Zuvie
    Matusek
Pascal Vine
Amrei Voigt
Stephanie Volk
David Von Bargen
Dan Wade
Megan Walker
Mike Walker
Sara Wallcraft

Katie Walter
Rowan Walters-Brunt
David Warden
H.R. Warren
Gina Watts
Tyler Waugh
Reid Webb
Mia Webster
Chris Weigert
Jason Weight
Rachel Weiner
Zack Wheeler
Kathryn Whidden
Cameron White
Saeshia White
Vivian Williams
Colleen Williamsen
Braheem Wilson

Grenville Wilson
Brianna Wimberly
Anne E. Winship
Kindle Wolf
Lisa Wolf
Torin Wong
Wooko the dancing bibble
Christopher C. Wright
Alex Wyatt
Malwinka Wyra
Shafik Yaghmour
Fran Yeldham
Sonja Yrjölä
Catharine Yung
Sophia Z
Mat Zebrowski
Alex Zimmermann
Dois Gail Zulueta